THE RESILIENT PIONEERS

A history of the Elastic Rail Spike Company
and its associates

THE RESILIENT PIONEERS

A history of the
Elastic Rail Spike Company
and its associates

John Milligan

PAUL HARRIS PUBLISHING

ABERDEEN AND EDINBURGH

First published in 1975 by
Paul Harris Publishing

International Standard Book Number 0 904505 02 2

Printed in Scotland by Bell & Bain Ltd.

Contents

There are many people I should like to thank for the time and the help they have so willingly and unstintingly given during the gathering of material for this book. Particularly I want to express my gratitude to all those members of the management and the staff of the Elastic Rail Spike Company Limited Group, both at home and overseas, past and present, but for whose enthusiastic co-operation the following account could not have been written.

J.M.
London 1973

Illustrations

Line Drawings in the text   *Page*

A Glance over the Shoulder

Mining was, in the beginning, the mother of the railways. Those primitive stretches of timber-plank track which materialised among Germany's Harz Mountains around 1556 owed their existence to the local ore mines which they served. And the first 'railways' in this country, which were beginning to appear in the north-east within fifty years, were built to smooth the transit of coal from the mines to the banks of the Tyne and the Wear. By the 1670s, in Northumberland, "five chaldrons of coal could be drawn by horses along wooden rails from the colliery to the river Tyne", while at Woolaton Colliery near Nottingham a gentleman named Huntingdon Beaumont had fixed up a similar arrangement right back in 1603. In 1700 there was scarcely a coal mine in England which did not boast a 'rayle-way'.

The group of companies whose story is recorded here was born and grew up in the railway engineering field, where it can now be said to be enjoying the prime of its life. And curiously the old relationship between the mines and the railways has, as the story will show, been renewed. The Elastic Rail Spike Company Ltd. Group is today a member of the Charter Consolidated family of companies. And Charter is something of a name in the mining world. Furthermore, the Elastic Rail Spike Company Ltd. Group now has a subsidiary of its own which is concerned with the manufacture and marketing of roof bolts for the mining industry. The wheel, as you might say, has come full circle.

But it is important to start at the beginning, and briefly to survey the background from which the original company's raison d'etre, the Elastic Rail Spike itself, sprang. The name, at least to the outsider, may have sounded droll: the product that bore it was not. It was, indeed, when all was said and done, simply a small piece of steel. Yet it ushered in an entirely new era in rail fastenings.

In order to understand this, it is not necessary to trace every single ancestor of the modern rail fastening. Yet the family history of the rail is worth a backward glance.

Developments in rail design came thick and fast during the eighteenth and nineteenth centuries. Because wooden rails were rather short on longevity, it soon became the practice to fix iron plates on top of them. An ironworks proprietor in Shropshire named William Reynolds, finding himself with a hefty stock of pig-iron he was not sure what to do with, decided in 1767 to lay it bar by bar on his wooden rails. His trucks had flanged wheels which neatly fitted against the 4-inch-wide bars. Flat cast-iron rails came in during the next decade, the first ones showing up near Sheffield in 1776, and malleable iron rails were soon to follow.

To stop wagons coming off the rails, as they all too often did, an innovation was made. The standard rail became L-shaped, the flat part of the plate taking the wagon wheels while the upright—some two or three inches high—kept them from slipping off. Metal spikes secured the rail to stone sleepers. But this plate rail, as it was known, was itself superseded by a newcomer called the edge rail, the invention of William Jessop of the Butterley Ironworks. Jessop decided to transfer responsibility for keeping the wheels on the line from the rail to the wheels themselves, and in so doing set the style which rails have followed ever since. Wheels had now acquired flanges they were not to lose.

Progress, however, far from being smooth, followed a wildly erratic course. Wooden rails were still being laid at Newcastle-upon-Tyne as late as 1805. Trevithick's steam locomotive of 1804 succeeded with monotonous regularity in fracturing those cast-iron edge rails which had been designed to carry it between Penydarren and Abercynon in South Wales. It was simply too heavy for them. And Jessop had found himself forced to use the very plate rail he had made obsolete when he was building the Surrey Iron Railway from Wandsworth to Croydon a couple of years earlier.

It was George Stephenson who pushed the case for switching from cast-iron to malleable iron rails, and on the Liverpool and Manchester line he used 'fish-bellies' of this type, "the patent of Mr. Birkenshaw". The fish-bellied rail was supported by cast-iron chairs ('pedestals' as they were originally called), which were themselves held down by spikes driven six inches through oak plugs into stone sleepers. The name 'fish-belly' arose because the rail's bottom edge bulged except at the points where the chairs supported it. That undulating extra bulk was supposed to give extra strength. "The cope rail was wider than the under surface."

Joseph Locke was Stephenson's assistant on the Liverpool and Manchester project. And it was he who, as Engineer-in-Chief of the Grand Junction Railway five years later, first introduced a rail which was "equal in form at top and bottom". He seriously applied himself, moreover, as his biographer tells us, "to the mode of fastening rails, and to the wooden key, as well as to improving the form of the rail itself." Locke's I-shaped rail of 1835-37 vintage—the double-headed rail as it was dubbed—was, like the fish-belly, laid on chairs secured to stone blocks. The idea behind the double heads was ingenious to say the least. When the upper head became worn all you did, in theory, was to turn the rail length upside down and— presto! you had a new head. Not surprisingly, this cunning development did not work. For the reserve head resting in the chair "was subjected to so much strain and friction that it wore out nearly as fast as the head carrying the traffic."

All the same, this type of rail had come to stay. With the size and weight of its head increased, it transformed itself into the bull-headed rail which by 1858 was in general use in Britain, keyed up in chairs fixed to timber sleepers. The head and the foot were of the same width, but the head was deeper. Keys of oak or teak held the rail in the cast-iron chairs. Fastening the chairs to the sleepers you had chair screws, or 'through bolts' (each consisting of bolt, nut and washer plate), or metal spikes driven through trenails (hollow pieces of wood like rawlplugs). The chief virtue of the bull-headed rail, in the eyes of those who first settled for it, was that when it was keyed up in its chairs "strong lateral support" resulted "with a large bearing area on the sleepers."

Originally the foot of the rail was curved to fit its chair, but by the 1930s it had become flat.

At the same time as Locke was devising the bull-headed section's forerunner, the double-headed rail, other engineers were also trying to solve the problem he had tackled. "A decision as to the best form of rail had then become a subject of general importance . . . together with the kindred question of 'sleepers'," as the son of Charles Vignoles put it in the biography of his father.

Vignoles was an ex-army officer, Irish-born but of Huguenot descent, whose highly adventurous life had started unusually early. Taken prisoner of war by the French in the West Indies when still in the equivalent of nappies, he obtained his commission as an ensign in the 43rd Foot at the absurd age of eighteen months. This was the only way the British commander could arrange for the toddler to be released from captivity. His later achievements included a survey of South Carolina and the invention of a method of ascending steep slopes on railways. It was while he was engaged upon the Sheffield, Ashton-under-Lyne and Manchester railway that he "fixed upon the form of rail . . . which has been almost universally

1. Primitive timber rails with timber sleepers.

2. Fishbelly rail on stone block sleeper.

3. L-shaped vertical channel rail.

HULL & HOLDERNESS – 1854

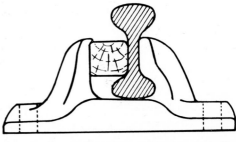

4. Double-headed rail, forerunner of the bull-head, held in cast-iron chair by wooden key.

5. The Elastic Rail Spike in Nigeria. John Agbon, engineer with the Nigerian Railways Corporation, gauging track.

6. Spikes taking the weight. River Class loco bearing down on ERS track in Nigeria.

adopted on the Continent and in many British Colonies, also largely in India and in the United States of America." On May 20th 1836 he referred to it for the first time in his diary. The following year the 'Vignoles rail' had started making an appearance. It was a flat-bottomed rail, with a very wide foot, and it was spiked direct to the sleeper.

"Every day's experience convinces me", he wrote, "of the propriety of laying the rails altogether on baulks of wood placed longitudinally; and by rolling a rail of 50 lbs weight into the annexed form, I dispense with the use of chairs, and obtain a better fastening, simple and less expensive. A railway thus laid will cost about £1,000 per mile less than one laid on stone blocks with cast-iron chairs; the repairs would be very much less, and a great saving would accrue in the diminished wear and tear not only of the railway itself, but principally of the engines and carriages passing over the same, from the smoothness of the motion and the absence of vibration".

But the Vignoles rail never caught on in England. The directors of the Sheffield, Ashton-under-Lyne & Manchester Railway Company were in league against him. He lost his job (being replaced by Locke) together with a cool £80,000 (his bosses sued him). Nor was Robert Stephenson, Engineer-in-Chief of the London and Birmingham Railway, exactly co-operative. "Mr. Stephenson having informed me that an order has been made for taking up the experimental rails laid on longitudinal wood sleepers near Harrow, I have, with the assistance of Mr. Woodhouse, made a minute examination of the state of the parts of the road so laid", Vignoles reported. He felt the trial had been eminently satisfactory. "Moreover, the extreme facility and of course economy of repair, and particularly of adjustment, are evident to the humblest workman."

Technical reasons were advanced, naturally, to support the general condemnation of the new flat-bottomed rail. The dogspikes which secured it to the sleepers were thought, for example, to be quite inadequate. And the rail was harder to roll.

Vignoles went off to Europe and sold his idea there. He kept a standing staff in Russia for five or six years, turning in the world's longest suspension bridge (over the Dnieper at Kiev) along with his railway projects. He became railway adviser to the Kingdom of Württemberg. He built railways in Switzerland, Spain, Poland and Brazil.

There was little doubt that the flat-bottomed rail would find favour in the United States. An even earlier f.b. rail than that invented by Vignoles had, in fact, been devised back in 1831 by Robert L. Stevens, president of the Camden and Amboy Railroad & Transportation Company. Initially this was spiked into wooden plugs fixed in stone sleepers, but one day the supply of stone ran dry and so timber crossties were laid instead, with the spikes driven straight into them. The result was a more flexible track, and one that offered a smoother ride.

In America the spikes were referred to as 'nails'. Often the initials of the railroad company were marked on the head of the nail, and fodder was thus unwittingly provided for railway relic hunters of the future.

One contemporary of Locke and Vignoles who attempted to take rail design in a completely different direction was the highly individualistic Brunel. For the Great Western Railway, to which he was appointed Engineer in 1833, "he preferred that peculiar shape which was called the 'bridge rail' ". This was bolted to longitudinal timber sleepers through holes in its flat side flanges, and there were no chairs. Lengths of Brunel's eccentric rail can be seen today, although not on the track. They are to be found used as fencing material in many parts of the West Country.

However, "because British railroad builders were pioneers,

they incurred the costs and burdens of all pioneers," as the historian David Thomson noted, "and paid the price for technical experiments and mistakes that other countries were able to avoid".

The bull-headed rail became the standard section on all railways in Britain, and it was to stay that way for ninety years, first in iron and then steel form. This was in spite of the fact that, without any base of its own, it relied upon the support of chairs—to which it was secured by wooden keys that tended to fall out. Everywhere else, the flat-bottomed rail had been used more or less from the very start. It was stronger, stiffer, and distributed the load more widely. Fewer components were needed in the sleeper assembly and the cost of maintenance was less. Chairs were replaced by more efficient steel or cast-iron baseplates.

The fastenings for both types of rail were all rigid. And as both the speed and the axle load of trains rapidly increased, engineers began to devote their attention to the reactions of the rail in these circumstances. The natural three-way movement of rails became more and more exaggerated. You had movement from side to side, which if unchecked would upset the gauge of the track. You had it longways. And you had it up and down. The problem was, how to bring these various tendencies under control. The need began to be felt for a quite new type of rail fastening which instead of being rigid would be flexible, or resilient.

It was from this need that the pattern of events leading to the formation of the Elastic Rail Spike Company took its cue.

An Invention born from Creosote

At the turn of the century the United States was something of a
paradise for a man with Oscar Max Bernuth's stock-in-trade.
This wealthy New York merchant was an importer of creosote.
The appetite of the numerous American railroad companies
for coal-tar creosote was almost insatiable. Amongst them they
shared 193,346 miles of track, bedded down on millions of
timber crossties, which is the transatlantic way of saying
sleepers. And expansion was moving at such a pace that by
1910 the overall mileage was up to 240,293. "Of course",
an American journalist was able to write, "we built railroads.
Enough miles of them to carry us to the moon."

Back in the 1830s that doughty pioneer Vignoles had reported
that wooden sleepers should be "either charred on the surface
or impregnated under hydrostatic pressure with coal- or
gas-tar, or else kyanized"—preserved by means of corrosive
sublimate—"in the tanks prepared, according to the process
now patented," if they were to last any length of time. Thirty
years later it was authoritatively announced in England that
imported timber required to be creosoted. ("Hitherto, the
sleepers have been of seasoned native larch, as the most durable,
but latterly, from the growing scarcity and cost of this article,
sleepers have been made of imported timbers from ports in the
Baltic.")

The distillation of coal-tar known as creosote oil quickly
became the railway sleeper's standard initiation drink. In
due course it was to increase the expectation of life of a sleeper
in the United States to upwards of thirty years. It was astute
of O. M. Bernuth to buy at such a moment the patent

for a revolutionary new process for impregnating timber in bulk.

One of the standard methods of creosoting at the time has been described as haphazard, and so it was. You simply dunked your sleepers in a creosote bath and left them there until you guessed that they had absorbed their fill. This, of course, depended on the kind of wood. A Douglas Fir sleeper needed a gallon and a half, whereas one made from Baltic Redwood took twice as much. Another method was simply to put the sleepers upright in a barrel, like telegraph poles, to soak up the oil, and then turn them the other way up to complete the process.

There was, indeed, a more scientific method which was both widely used and fairly successful. This was the Bethell process, a pressure treatment which had been patented in England as long ago as 1838. After drying your timber in stacks and then sawing it to size, you fed it into a long, air-tight cylinder (latterly made of steel) by the truck-load. Doors at each end of the massive tube were shut and bolted, and steam pipes within the cylinder brought up the temperature to some 170°F. while at the same time air was pumped out. Then the timber now being dry, you pumped in creosote oil from tanks underneath until the pressure was up to 200 lb to the square inch. The pores of the timber opened, and the oil was forced into every cell. This 'full-cell' process is still the method favoured in Britain.

But around 1900 creosote oil had become unduly expensive in the States, so much so that in due course other substances began to be mixed with it, especially for the treatment of crossties (sleepers), with a resultant loss of preservative value. Somehow a way had to be found to reduce the cost of timber preservation. Max Rüping was a German engineer who not only appreciated this but also was aware that his own country had plenty of creosote to spare and could export it. He devised the 'empty-cell' process, which consisted of using a large quantity of creosote to impregnate the wood, and then recovering most of it so that you ended up with a "smaller final retention of the preservative" than was usually the case. This was important because, in the treatment of crossties, although penetration needed to be deepish, only moderate retention was necessary.

What Rüping did was to apply air pressure to the wood before the creosote oil was injected. Some of the air was forced into the timber and became trapped there when the cylinder filled up with oil. The pressure was then stepped up, so that the creosote was driven into the wood, and the air already there became yet more compressed. When the pressure was taken off, the oil drained out of the cylinder and at the same time the compressed air in the wood expelled a further quantity of preservative. A high vacuum finished off the process, hurrying up the recovery of the oil. The result was that, with a limited retention, you were able to achieve deeper penetration in permeable timber than you could with any existing process.

It was in 1904 that Rüping sold this idea to O. M. Bernuth, although he had obtained the American patent for it two years earlier. Bernuth rapidly developed the Rüping Process in the States, where it was introduced the following year, and where it was soon to become "the principal creosoting process in use". He also developed a bright idea of his own, becoming the first man to go in for the bulk shipment of creosote oil by tanker. Chartering a 10,000-ton tanker, the SS *Pectan*, from the Gas, Light & Coke Company, he shipped a trial load back home. It reached Galveston, Texas, on December 17th, 1904. He made such a killing that he just had to go on. What he now began to do was to charter a tanker to carry crude oil from the U.S.A. to Europe, and to fill up with creosote oil for the return trip. Most of that creosote found its way into American railroad sleepers.

Teaming up with George Lembcke, brother of a friend he

used to play gridiron football with, Bernuth formed a company specifically to handle this new business. Bernuth, Lembcke Co., Inc. was incorporated in New York State in 1907.

Bernuth had a very close friend who ran the Chipman Chemical Company of New Jersey. It so happened that in 1923 this man's son, Ralph Chipman, who was on familiar enough terms with Bernuth to call him 'Uncle', came along saying he was in desperate need of help. He had come unstuck in a bid to gain control of the arsenic market and was in the red to the tune of 400,000 dollars. 'Uncle' remembered a time when he had himself been saved from disaster by a sudden anonymous gift of a thousand dollars. So what could he do but come to the rescue now? He bought the Chipman Chemical Company, and promptly reorganised it.

Both Bernuth and his partner George Lembcke felt the need for a firm footing in England to help their business operate at full pressure. Lembcke paid a visit to London during 1927. An Austrian who had migrated long ago to the States, Lembcke was fluent in half a dozen languages and a man of enormous charm. One day he arranged to have lunch with an English oil man named Lancelot Newling Rawes. They met at Lombard's in the City. By three o'clock that afternoon the Lembcke magic had triumphed, and at the same time Rawes' innate gift for seizing an opportunity had not let him down. When he rose from the table L. N. Rawes knew that he was leaving his present job at that very moment and that he would start first thing in the morning with Bernuth, Lembcke Company, Inc.

Rawes became the Manager of the American company's London office, although it was not until the following year that he met O. M. Bernuth himself. The two men got on well, and by 1929 Rawes found himself at the helm of a new company, a British subsidiary of the Chipman Chemical Company. It was started with £100-worth of capital, and its function was to provide timber preservatives and weedkillers for the railways.

Amongst these was a powerful solution based on calcium chloride, used for keeping weeds in check in railway ballast. Companies like the L.M.S. and the L.N.E.R. required weedkiller in considerable quantities. It was sprayed on the track at the rate of 400 gallons to the mile. Between five and seven parts of the liquid, indeed, was water, yet the 'spray train's' tank truck took a couple of thousand gallons of concentrated chemical solution on each trip. So the prospect seemed good for the new company. Within three years, however, its losses amounted to £6,000. Rawes advised Bernuth to wind it up.

Bernuth had not been a rugged player of American football for nothing. Fighting spirit he had in plenty. Ignoring his lieutenant's recommendation he turned the ailing subsidiary into a public company. To begin with there were only three shareholders. But one of them was I.C.I. And soon Burmah Oil made a fourth. Rawes was able to continue forging links with the railways. He became good friends with J. C. L. Train, Chief Engineer of the L.N.E.R., and with W. K. Wallace, Chief Engineer of the L.M.S.

Meanwhile in Germany someone else had been making the most of his railway contacts. The inventor of the Rüping Process for creosoting sleepers was by now held in high esteem by the German railway engineering fraternity. So when Rüping came up with invention number two—a resilient rail fastening—not surprisingly the German railways expressed an immediate interest. By 1934 several test tracks had been laid, including one at Schwerte, just outside Dörtmund, in which Rüping's 'schienennägel' (rail spikes) performed the dual job of holding the flat-bottomed rail to the baseplates on which they rested and the baseplates to the sleepers.

These spring spikes represented a striking advance in permanent way technology. Back in 1837 Vignoles had lamented "the fruitless attempt to obtain a perfectly non-elastic

railway" in which he admitted he had himself participated before devising his flat-bottomed rail. But virtually a
century later rail fastenings themselves were still rigid. The
need for something resilient had begun to be felt in railway
engineering quarters, since trains were getting faster and rails,
which had always moved a little beneath the weight of a
moving train, were moving more.

Rüping's spike was made of spring steel of superior quality,
and designed so that its head would flex as the rail moved and
would keep a firm and constant grip on the rail foot, main-
taining a pressure of some 800 lb there if correctly driven.
The idea was, furthermore, that it would not work its way out
of the sleeper however tough the traffic conditions.

Sensibly, Rüping took out world patents for his invention.
At the same time he wrote to his old friend Bernuth in New
York, telling him about the spike and suggesting that it might
well be worth developing in the United States. He knew
Bernuth had multifarious connections with American railroad
companies as a result of the creosote business.

Bernuth came over to London, picked up Rawes and went on
to Germany to look at the test track at Schwerte. They were
impressed. But they turned the spike down. There was no
hope, after all, of trying to sell it in Britain since all the rails
here were bull-headed, and Rüping's spike was designed
for flat-bottomed track. Certainly there was no such obstacle in
the States, but there another type of fastening, the square
dogspike with a large head, was in such widespread use that
getting a foot in the market would be exceptionally difficult.

But later that same year, 1934, Max Rüping paid a visit
to New York. Bernuth entertained him to dinner at his luxur-
ious apartment in Number 510 Park Avenue. Rüping came
out with the news that he had received an offer for his patents
on the rail spike, and that all he had to do was put his signature
to the agreement. This was too much for Bernuth. It was time

for him to move in, and move in fast. Then and there he agreed to buy the patents for both North and South America.

The next thing was that Bernuth and Rüping decided to form a company to develop and market their Elastic Rail Spike. They called it The Elastic Rail Spike Corporation Incorporated, and by 1935 four million spikes had been sold to the New York Central Railroad. The steel came from the mighty mills of Pittsburgh, which was where the spikes themselves were manufactured.

It was in the late summer of 1936 that L. N. Rawes turned up at 510 Park Avenue. Before leaving he stuffed a sample Elastic Rail Spike in his pocket with the idea of showing it around when he got back home. The moment he did return he paid a call, in the course of his business in connection with creosote and weedkillers, upon his friend Bill Wallace of the L.M.S. Producing his spike, he showed it to Wallace who after examining it closely, said "It's good, get it patented!"

Rawes had timed his visit well, albeit fortuitously, for Wallace was about to put down several lengths of flat-bottomed test track for the L.M.S. He had himself recently been in the States to have a look at the railways and had been very impressed with the track he had seen there. Later he was to record: "It was noticed that track on American lines had stood up to traffic with minimum maintenance through the severe financial depression during the middle thirties in the U.S.A., and it was considered that a test should be made in this country of American flat-bottomed track to see if it required less maintenance than the standard bull-head."

Along with the flat-bottomed rail Wallace had decided to try out five different types of rail fastening. These "ranged from bolts and screws, somewhat similar to the standard permanent way in Germany, to a mushroom-headed screw . . . ." All were rigid, and all originated overseas.

As to the Elastic Rail Spike, what a pity it was that Rawes

had not brought this one up sooner, because he would have tried it, said Wallace. "Is it really too late?" replied the indomitable Rawes. "Well, these things take months and months to organise, and all the homework has been done, you know", responded the Chief Engineer of the L.M.S. "However", he added, after something of a pause, "how soon can you get 5,000?"

In next to no time, Rawes was on the telephone to Rüping. Krupps of Essen, it appeared, were able to make the spikes and they would need six weeks. The deal was on.

On the morning of Sunday, December 13th 1936, it was snowing hard in Putney. The reign of George VI was three days' old. Rawes left home early. He was on his way to see Wallace's first piece of flat-bottomed track with Elastic Rail Spikes holding it down. Test tracks had been installed at West Hampstead, Mill Hill and Cricklewood, on the old Midland line, and at Harlington in Bedfordshire. Well, there they were. Wallace had kept to his word. Now it was up to the spikes to prove themselves.

Even before they had had time to do so, people started showing interest. They included G.K.N. who had thoughts of India in their minds. But it was Wallace's intention to give his test lengths twelve months in which, as you might say, to show their mettle.

December 1937 arrived. The Elastic Rail Spike appeared to have put itself at the top of Wallace's list. For one thing it was very simple, far simpler than the sophisticated fastening used by the German railways, and for another it was cheaper than its competitors. But above all it seemed to be doing its job with admirable efficiency. It held the rail down better than the rigid fastenings, and rail creep—the habit rails have of moving in the same direction as the traffic they carry does—simply just did not occur. To support its case, there was by now a successful record of use in both Germany and the United

States. So far, then, so good, but further test work over a
period of years would be needed before the L.M.S. could
commit itself to adopting the spike.

For quite some time now Rawes had acquired the habit of
undertaking regular tours which took him to Scotland, first
to see the Divisional Engineer of the L.M.S. (Scottish Region),
A. H. McMurdo in Glasgow—father of A. W. McMurdo,
the present Chief Civil Engineer of British Railways—and
then to visit his L.N.E.R. counterpart in Edinburgh, a somewhat dour Scot called Fraser. Rawes, it transpired, was the
only commercial man W. A. Fraser would readily consent to
lunch with.

One day back in the early autumn of 1937, somewhere in
Edinburgh a luncheon table was prepared for Fraser and his
sassenach guest. When he got there, Rawes found that Fraser
was not alone. With him he had a colleague whose name, it
seemed, was Stewart Sanson. Priding himself on his nose for
likely talent, Rawes determined that he would follow up this
young man.

The man in question had been with the Civil Engineering
department of the L.N.E.R. since 1926. Before that he had
taken a First Class honours degree in Civil Engineering at
Edinburgh University. Subsequently he had won the Institution
of Civil Engineers' James Forrest Medal with his paper on
railway permanent way. As a result of practical track experience
he had come to believe that existing bull-head track would not
take the high speed heavy traffic that was to come. A switch to
flat-bottomed track in Britain was, he felt, inevitable and the need
would then arise for a new resilient rail fastening which would
provide far more elasticity than conventional rigid fastenings
could. Such was Britain's permanent way of the future as he
envisaged it. Of high speed traffic, what is more, it could be said
that he knew something. There had been those high speed running
tests of the *Silver Jubilee* train which was to cut the journey

time between London and Edinburgh down to six hours. He had seen how the track stood up to them.

Impressed, Rawes returned to London. But it was not long before he was on the telephone, inviting Sanson down for the weekend. Sanson came. After playing a round at the Royal Wimbledon Golf Club, Rawes broached the subject that was in his mind. Would Sanson be willing to join him, and start a new company to develop a resilient rail fastening? Well he knew that such a project would be close to his quarry's heart. And of one thing Rawes was unswervingly convinced. The new company was going to be run by a real railwayman, if it was ever to get anywhere.

"We'll talk further in the morning, after breakfast" said Rawes—"after you've decided. You're better off staying with the railway, where you'll be Chief Engineer one day, inevitably. But if you want to come out into the hard cold world, here's your chance."

The next day the two men reached a satisfactory agreement. And so it was that Sanson gave up his post as Personal Assistant to the Divisional Engineer of the L.N.E.R.'s Scottish Area, said goodbye to a brilliant future as a railway engineer, and moved south. The new company he joined was incorporated on 8th October 1937, under the name of Elastic Rail Spike Company Limited. Its registered office was at Cory Buildings, 117, Fenchurch Street, London, E.C.3.

Financially, the bulwark of the new company was O. M. Bernuth, who took up 45% of the shares in the name of Bernuth, Lembcke Company, Inc. Rawes took up ten per cent, while the remaining 45% went to Max Rüping as remuneration in return for all the patents he was throwing in. Bernuth, having already bought the patents for North and South America, was unwilling to pay cash for any others. Indeed, had it not been for Rawes' bulldozing tactics he would not have participated in the venture at all. He had told Rawes earlier,

"You can keep your spikes! I don't want to hear any more about them." Audaciously Rawes was soon to respond, "You're in! I've bought you 45% of the shares."

London was chosen as the place from which to run the new operation, largely because it was felt that Britain was the centre of the railway world, with its finger in the pie everywhere from Africa to India and Argentina.

At the first meeting of the directors, held in Leadenhall Street on October 12th, the solicitor William Hill Newson was appointed Chairman. Of the other directors, only L. N. Rawes was present—O. M. Bernuth and his son Patrick being in New York and Max Rüping in Frankfurt. The minutes of the meeting were recorded in the meticulous copperplate handwriting of the Company Secretary, a Scots chartered accountant named Thomas Johnston who had been with Bernuth, Lembcke Co., Inc. in London since 1930.

On December 8th Rüping attended his one and only board meeting. Twelve days later Rawes was made Managing Director, and L. S. Sanson's appointment as Manager was confirmed with effect from November 25th 1937.

During that same November, a thousand Elastic Rail Spikes arrived from Essen in Germany. Sanson's career as a super-salesman was about to begin.

The Spike takes a Grip

In 1937 bull-headed track still lorded it over the landscape of Britain. All four of the major railway companies used it. The L.M.S. had put down its test lengths of flat-bottomed track at the end of the previous year, and soon afterwards the L.N.E.R. had followed suit, using the Elastic Rail Spike as a fastening. But it was clear there would be no real chance here in the immediate future of marketing spikes designed for flat-bottomed track. Overseas, however, the picture was different. Just about every country in the world that boasted a railway system had from the start gone on to the 'f.b.' standard.

It was clear to Stewart Sanson that any commercial development would have to begin abroad. The slogan he adopted was "Export or die!" So, in the New Year of 1938, off he went on his travels. He arrived in Cape Town, with no one specific to call on, no contacts pre-arranged. He travelled throughout the Union, stormed the railway engineering citadels of Johannesburg and Salisbury, trekked up northwards beyond the Rhodesias, with an Elastic Rail Spike or two in his suitcase and little else. Gradually, as he worked his way up through the continent, he sold the idea, and soon agreements to instal test track began to blossom in many parts of Africa.

For a first attempt, it was a pretty successful sales safari. Back in London Sanson devoted himself to technical questions of design. He prepared all the original drawings, and the first technical bulletins, himself. Then there was the question of manufacture to consider. Until now the company had obtained its spikes—the few thousands it had been able to sell

19

—from Germany. If costs were to be contained, somebody had to start making them here.

Sanson went up to Sheffield, armed with a specimen spike, to see whom he could find who would make a replica of it. Shopping around, he went to see the firm of George Turton, Platts & Co. Ltd. in Meadowhall Road. The things they made in their normal line of business were self-contained buffers for locomotives and other railway vehicles, spiral springs, drop-stamping and hollow forgings. But they also had a Permanent Way Department which, over three shifts, employed two hundred and fifty men, and which produced among other items steel keys for bull-headed track. The Engineer was a man named Sanderson. But it was with the Foreman that Sanson somehow established a rapid rapport.

Sam Oldfield was transparently a full-blooded railway engineer who really knew what he was talking about. He had joined Turton, Platts twenty-three years before, in 1915, after serving his apprenticeship with Easterbrook, Allcard & Co. Ltd. who were general engineers in Sheffield. Sanson showed him an Elastic Rail Spike and said "Can you make this?" After scrutinising it for a few moments Sam looked up and replied, "I think so."

The Yorkshireman had no tools to help him. He made his first spike by hand. It went into the furnace five or six times, which did not do the steel much good. But the replica was produced, and Sam sent it to London. Back came an order for six more like it. So he set to and made a tool for the spike. He found that the sliding movement, when he was shaping the head of the spike, wore the tool away. His answer was to get some stellite and weld some 3/16 in. to $\frac{1}{4}$ in. of it on to the tool. Rawes and Sanson judged the spikes he produced to be satisfactory.

George Turton, Platts received a contract for manufacturing Elastic Rail Spikes. They put in new furnaces. And there was a

7. 'Pandrol' with rejuvenated steel sleepers in Nigeria. At Gerti Station on the Kloof.

8. Elastic Rail Spikes 6,000 feet underground, on a mine track in South Africa.
Reproduced by courtesy of the Mine Manager, Western Deep Levels Ltd.

9. 'Pandrol' *in situ* in its country of origin. On Norwegian State Railways' track with concrete sleepers.

10. The factory at the Forge. An aerial view of Claylands Forge, Worksop.

problem here. The raw material for the spikes was silico-manganese steel. From time to time, at any rate at the outset, you had to test the steel by breaking it, and if the fractures were too coarse you knew the heating was not right. Over-heating resulted in a very coarse fracture. The upshot was the decision that all the furnaces had to be automatically controlled in order to maintain the correct heat.

Sanderson, as the Engineer at the Sheffield works, might have been expected to have designed the tooling for the spikes. In fact he left the responsibility for doing so in the capable hands of Sam Oldfield. And before long orders were running into the thousands.

Sanson's export drive was bearing fruit. Following his African trip, he went to the United States and then sailed on to Australia and New Zealand. In America he inspected a number of stretches of test track where the Elastic Rail Spikes produced by the original transatlantic company were busily proving themselves.

After saying goodbye to San Francisco he undertook the same kind of safari in the Antipodes as he had accomplished in Africa, without any contacts having been arranged in advance. He headed for Broken Hill in New South Wales, where that huge outcrop of ironstone laced with silver and lead ore had once enticed its quota of gold seekers. But Sanson went there to visit Broken Hill Proprietary Company Ltd., Australia's number one steelmakers. He wanted to know if they would make him some spikes, enough to cope with the Australian market he knew he would soon have up his sleeve. Adamantly they replied that they would not. Sanson, however, decided to ship a few tons of their steel back to Sheffield just to see if it was suitable.

In his attempt to get manufacture under way on the other side of the world, on that occasion Sanson failed. But he sold the gospel of the Elastic Rail Spike. Orders for test track soon

c

came in from both Australia and New Zealand, not to speak of Malaya, Siam, Burma, India and Egypt. Down under—where each state had its own railway system—New South Wales, Victoria and Western Australia were interested.

Nor did the frenetic search for overseas markets represent the only development in the company at this time. A major design modification was introduced. The original Elastic Rail Spike—Type A as it became known—was driven through a hole in a large double-shoulder cast-iron baseplate resting on a softwood sleeper. It secured both rail and baseplate to the sleeper. What Sanson now devised was a twisted spike (Type T). The head twisted to one side of the shaft.

The significance of this development was that the rail could now rest right up against the shaft of the spike, and the grip of the spike was therefore greatly strengthened. (The shaft of the A Type had been driven well clear of the rail foot, and at right angles to it.) It also meant that with hardwood sleepers, a baseplate could even be dispensed with as often as not. Here was an innovation which instantly appealed to railwaymen abroad.

The application for a grant of an English patent ("in respect of a new type of spike incorporating a twisted neck or oblique gripping arm") was discussed at a company board meeting on March 31st 1939. By April 5th, applications on behalf of the 'Twisted Neck Spike' were all ready for take-off.

The April of 1939 saw Sanson embarking upon the third of his mammoth sales journeys. And this was to be a round-the-world affair. The opportunity to travel freely might not, after all, last much longer. Since the Munich Agreement of the previous September, clouds of crisis had continued to darken the international sky. On April 7th Italian troops invaded Albania, and some six weeks later Mussolini and Hitler were to sign their Pact of Steel.

Hither and thither Sanson scurried, making contacts,

eliciting promises, building up goodwill. It was his persistent policy to seek out the Chief Engineer himself whenever he visited a railway company and to convince him about the economics of using the Elastic Rail Spike. It was no use, he felt, relying upon management to appreciate and act upon such advice. If you really wanted progress, you went straight to the man who counted most. The responsibility for track safety was a cross the Chief Engineer had to bear, and he always

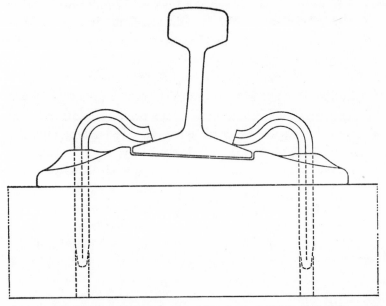

Fig. 1. British Railways BR2 Assembly with Type A Elastic Rail Spikes and cast-iron baseplates.

ended up by choosing the fastenings *he* thought were right, regardless of what anyone else in his company suggested.

In July two gentlemen with the names of Dr. Kuo and Mr. Yang became official 'advisers in respect of China.' Agents had been lined up in Johannesburg (for South Africa, Northern and Southern Rhodesia) and Bangkok.

By September, spikes had started arriving in Malaya and

Australia, and test tracks were due to be installed in Argentina. All five of the Argentine railway companies had offices in London, which certainly helped liaison, and Sanson's passage was booked to Buenos Aires so that he could be on the spot to give expert help.

So it was that the seeds of progress were sown. At home, the L.M.S. added further trial lengths to supplement those it had installed in 1936. Another eleven miles of flat-bottomed track was laid on the main line near Crewe and Elastic Rail Spikes were included amongst the fastenings. Of the six types originally chosen for testing, only three were now effectively in the running, and the Elastic Rail Spike was one of them.

In a paper read during 1939 before the Permanent Way Institution, N. W. Swinnerton of the L.M.S. gave an account of the experiments his company had been carrying out and singled out the spike for particular praise. In championing the cause of the flat-bottomed rail itself, he showed that contrary to general belief, it could be laid just as quickly as bull-headed track. You simply fastened your baseplates to the sleepers, instead of bolting chairs to them, before fitting the rail.

Sanson's prediction of years before that flat-bottomed track would have to come looked as though it was soon to be fulfilled.

War, and then no Steel

The outbreak of war did not put a stop to Sanson's globetrotting. It simply changed its character. Instead of going to Buenos Aires in September 1939 he went to France—in uniform. He arrived there before hostilities were a week old.

The Army was not new to him, for he had been commissioned in the Royal Engineers as a territorial as long ago as 1926, and had transferred only the previous year to the Regular Army Reserve. During the dark pre-Dunkirk days of 1940 he was in command of a Regular Army railway construction company across the Channel, and he was to be preoccupied with railway and dockworks engineering and operation throughout the rest of the war. Posted to India, he became responsible for rail movement there, being mentioned in despatches "for gallant and distinguished services in operations in Burma and North-East India in 1943". June 7th 1945 saw him taking on the duties of D.D.Tn. (Deputy Director of Transportation), Calcutta, with the rank of full Colonel. This was effectively the senior and most important executive transportation job in India Command.

He emerged from the war, in fact, with his reputation as a railway engineer considerably boosted. And his distinctive ability to focus all his energy upon one problem at a time had been given six years' valuable exercise. He had also enlarged his circle of engineering contacts. One new friend he made was Lt. Col. Peter Davies, O.B.E., R.E., who, upon leaving the Regular Army some time after the war, was himself to join the Elastic Rail Spike Company.

25

But back in the autumn of 1939 the company was losing able men, not acquiring them. Even the Chairman, W. H. Newson, now wore the uniform of a Lieutenant Colonel and was able only occasionally to attend a board meeting. On April 22nd 1940 L. N. Rawes was appointed to the chair in his place.

A tricky situation arose in connection with the 9,000 £1 shares in the company held by Max Rüping, the original inventor of the Elastic Rail Spike. In Newson's legal view, the agreements with Rüping had automatically been dissolved the moment war was declared. The shares had been impounded by the Custodian of Enemy Property, whose job it was simply to protect them. It was possible that when the war was over "the Custodian would be directed to return enemy assets to their owners but it seemed more likely that, as the amount owed by Germany to this country far exceeded our debt to Germany, legislation would be introduced to enable the Custodian to sell enemy assets to meet British claims against Germany". Newson voiced this opinion in a letter on May 3rd 1943, at a time when the Allies had just contrived a major victory over the Germans and Italians in Tunisia. Had he been writing two or three years earlier, it is doubtful that he would have seemed so confident as to the ultimate outcome of the war.

At the next board meeting, in June 1943, Newson (by now returned to the fold) pointed out that, when the time came, the Custodian would be able neither to "obtain a fancy price for the shares" nor to sell them to "anyone other than the existing shareholders so long as they were willing to purchase at the fair value".

So, for the time being, a substantial amount of share capital was frozen, and thus it was to remain for two more gruelling years. By the time these were up, the company was financially just about out on its feet. A hefty demand for rail spikes had built up, yet it simply could not be met. An equally hefty injection of cash was vitally necessary, particularly since the

company now needed its own manufacturing plant yet could
not afford to buy it.

On June 14th 1945, some five weeks after V.E. Day, Rawes
informed the board that "he and Mr. Bernuth were not
disposed to subscribe further capital so long as enemy interest
existed and that, with the object of removing this obstacle, an
approach had been made to the Custodian of Enemy Property
with a view to the purchase of the Rüping shares." He added,
however, that "the Custodian had refused to consent to a sale",
and that as a result he had been discussing with Bernuth,
Lembcke Co., Inc. "the question of a reconstruction of the
company". Such a reconstruction was in the circumstances,
he felt, inevitable.

Nevertheless, efforts to retrieve the Rüping shares were not
abandoned. Their acquisition was essential, whatever happened.
A letter was sent on July 31st to the Trading with the Enemy
Department of the Treasury and Board of Trade, setting out
terms for the proposed reconstruction of the company in the
light of the no longer applicable agreements with Rüping.
The Custodian of Enemy Property was invited to an Extraordinary General Meeting of shareholders to be held on August
31st at 11 a.m.

The Custodian did not either accept or refuse the invitation.
On the appointed morning no one knew whether he would
turn up or not. At two minutes to eleven there was no sign of
him. But at one minute to, the Custodian's representative
arrived. He looked like a man who would readily give no
quarter where negotiations were concerned.

Rawes, as Chairman, addressed the meeting. The company
had, he said, "made a loss every year since its incorporation".
The figure at December 31st 1944 had been a loss of £16,612.
13s. 3d., or £9,593. 7s. 6d. before depreciation. The position
had not materially altered during the current year. The last
accounts, prepared up to June 30th, showed a loss of £16,498.

5*s*. 5*d*., or £8,921. 7*s*. 2*d*. before depreciation. There was, Rawes went on, no prospect of continuing without the introduction of fresh capital. The directors had made every effort to find a way of introducing fresh capital but without success. The alternatives were to attempt to carry on the way things were, or to reconstruct. It has been decided to reconstruct.

The capital structure of the new company was to be different, provision being made "for a nominal capital of £25,500, divided into Redeemable Preference shares and Ordinary shares". The directors were satisfied, insisted the Chairman, that the Ordinary shares "would be taken up when required and provide sufficient working capital so that there was every reasonable prospect of the company being in a position to trade successfully". There was certainly nothing wrong with the patents which were held. Enough profits ought to be earned, without too much trouble, for the Preference shares to be redeemed by the new company.

A resolution was then passed that the company should be wound up voluntarily, so that the reconstruction could be accomplished. After the meeting, Rawes buttonholed the Custodian's representative and asked him why he had bothered to come, since he had virtually said nothing. "I just came to find out if you were honest men", was the reply. "I have decided that you are, and we are selling now." He wanted to be sure he was going to be offered 6*s*. 8*d*. each for the shares which he held, but he did not intend to take shares in the new company.

The crisis was over. On September 14th the new Elastic Rail Spike Company Ltd. was incorporated, and its first board meeting was held four days later, with Rawes once more in the chair.

No contact was made with Rüping after the war. It appeared that he had not developed anything new in Germany. In the following New Year it was reported that he had died. The remaining German patent for the Elastic Rail Spike became the property of his widow, who between 1952 and her own death in 1959 received a pension from the company.

The American company, the Elastic Rail Spike Corporation Inc., had its own problem to face with regard to Rüping-held shares. In a letter to London dated January 23rd 1946, O. M. Bernuth talked of "the complex situation still existing between ERS Corporation and the U.S. Alien Property Custodian". This prevented progress in connection with the South American and Canadian patents for the spike, which were held by the New York company. For various reasons very little contact had been made with the Canadian territory, and the London company wanted permission to move in both there and in South America, being willing to pay a royalty on all sales that might result.

Yet the Argentine and Brazilian patents had themselves been taken over during the war by the Alien Property Custodian, who "for some reason which was not explained" still held them, although now empowered to return them. There seemed to be some confusion within the Custodian's Office, one section of which "appeared to be urging that they should be handed back. It was not clear why this deadlock continued". As to the shares, it appeared that they had been seized without official authority from the Government. The Custodian therefore was in the position of being unable either to sell them or to hand them back.

Bernuth was unwilling to pump in further capital. The demise of the American company consequently became inevitable. It had, in any case, never really made a go of things in a practical sense. There were several reasons for its failure to do so. It had never undertaken its own manufacturing. The spikes it sold were made in Pittsburgh, and the real cost of both manufacture and marketing had not been established, let alone appreciated. Sales were sparse enough at that, partly because selling and supervision were carried out by creosote salesmen without practical railway experience, and partly because traditional rail fastenings were so firmly entrenched in the States.

The lack of supervision when spikes were being installed may well have been a decisive factor. It was the American practice, with dogspikes, to hammer the spike into the wood of the sleeper as if it were a nail. Indeed, 'nail' was the very word used to describe a spike. With an Elastic Rail Spike, however, driving into a bored hole had to be done to a gauge if uniform pressure on the rail was to be achieved. Crude and faulty installation could hardly have been expected to enhance its popularity.

In London, Rawes was soon to insist that every one of his company's salesmen had to have honest to goodness railway experience up his sleeve.

Despite the fact that the original Elastic Rail Spike Company Ltd. had consistently made a loss, and that from the point of view of sales it had been forced to spend the war years more or less just ticking over, it had quietly maintained a record of some success. Never for one moment had Sanson's world view been relinquished. Export-mindedness thrived, and during a period when others might well have thought it folly. The company's eye was always on the morrow. In 1941, for example —on October 20th—it was decided that the registration of patents granted in India should be secured in relation to Burma also. Just over seven weeks later the Japanese invasion of the country was to begin. Some twenty-five years were to go by before the decision paid off. Which it did when 475,000 Elastic Rail Spikes were booked and bought by the Burmese.

80,000 spikes a year were exported in 1941 and 1942. The figure for 1940 had been 30,300. That for 1943 was 150,000. A major order came in from Katanga, in what was then the Belgian Congo, for SR.8 Spikes, through the intermediary offices of Rhodesia Railways. Between January and June 1943, 100,000 S.13 Spikes were sent out to Rhodesia itself. T.3 and T.4 Spikes, to be delivered at the rate of 50,000 a month, were "very urgently required for military purposes" in Nigeria.

Gradually the company was strengthening its grip. Testimonials were coming in. On May 3rd 1944 Rawes reported that he had recently met W. J. O. Reeves, Chief Engineer of the Nigerian Railway, who had been home on leave, and who had a mini-installation of 12,000 T.4 Spikes with which he was very pleased. The Nigerian Railway had been using the spike since early in 1940. Reeves had spoken of a derailment which happened at the approach to a trestle bridge on which the spikes were installed. "The adjoining steel-sleepered track had been badly torn up and, but for the holding power of the spikes, it was thought that the train would almost certainly have been thrown into the river."

It was just over a year later when the Assistant Engineer in charge of Nigerian Railways' relaying programme, Ronald Bridgman, wrote in about his problems with getting unskilled labour to drive the spike correctly. Very often the rail was hit instead of the spike head, and "his boys were unable easily to distinguish between right-hand and left-hand spikes". A solution was rapidly devised for that second problem. The company arranged for all left-hand spikes to be painted red, and for all bags containing left-hand spikes to bear a clearly recognisable red mark.

After a few months another letter arrived from Bridgman. "The boys have got the hang of driving the spikes now, and the hammer gang is quite good to watch . . . The red paint (used to indicate left-hand spikes) is fine and is much appreciated by us all."

Reports kept trickling in about test tracks which had been laid just before the war. After four years' service on the Cairo-Alexandria line of the Egyptian State Railways, a stretch

secured by 27,000 SR.10 Spikes had apparently entirely solved
the problem of rail creep. Trials undertaken by New Zealand
Railways and by the Commonwealth Railways of Australia had
proved more than satisfactory.

On umpteen locations, both at home and abroad, tiny
quantities of spikes were performing a valuable ambassadorial
role. The Director of Transportation at the War Office had
taken a mere 2,000 T.4 Spikes to see if they would control rail
creep in a steeply inclined track somewhere up north. A
thousand spikes were ordered for the Liverpool Overhead
Railway. And the Allied Post-War Requirements Bureau was
giving inquisitive sniffs. The Chairman of its Technical
Advisory Committee on Inland Transport, a Dutchman named
Professor E. R. Hondelink (who was later to join the board of
the ERS Company), had been in touch with Rawes for some
while and was quite interested in the spike.

November 1944 saw the company's one millionth spike
being invoiced, and a month or two later the Science Museum
in South Kensington was asking for an exhibit consisting of a
flat-bottomed rail and baseplate secured to a sleeper by Elastic
Rail Spikes.

Meanwhile, the L.M.S. test tracks which had been installed
in 1936 and 1939 were standing up well. In August 1943
Rawes accompanied N. W. Swinnerton of the L.M.S. and
three L.N.E.R. engineers on an inspection trip to see how the
installations at Blisworth and Weedon were doing. Afterwards
Bilham, one of the L.N.E.R. men, had written to the Chairman
and commented: "The flat bottom track that we saw was
certainly very impressive, the line and level being as near
perfection as one could hope to get, and it is evident that the
Elastic Spikes are doing their work in a thoroughly satisfactory manner".

The L.M.S. and the L.N.E.R. were working hand-in-glove
on the trials of the spike, and the latter were even using L.M.S.

baseplates and rail-joints to go with it. According to Swinnerton, the L.M.S. "had now established that, excluding the rail,
the set-up of flat-bottom rail and Elastic Rail Spike was initially
cheaper than the chair or any other form of bull-head or
flat-bottom arrangement, also the residual value of the heavy
flat-bottom rail was higher". He added that "the cost question
now tended to work in favour of the spike".

Late in 1943 there had been a derailment at Bakewell in
Derbyshire. It happened on a section of the line where flat-
bottomed track, secured by the spike, adjoined bull-head track
fixed in chairs. The flat-bottom track, reported Swinnerton,
stood up extraordinarily well, and the damage would have been
far worse had any other type of fastening been used. The spikes
were merely "twisted around", and many of them were still
holding. In only one case had there been any distortion of
gauge, and that was very slight. The bull-headed track, on
the other hand, had been completely wrecked.

The next thing was that the L.M.S. and the L.N.E.R. got
together still more closely to standardise components for flat-
bottomed track. They were to put down thirty-five miles of this
jointly, securing two-thirds of the trial track with the spike and
one-third with other kinds of fastening. The L.N.E.R. was
doing twenty miles and the L.M.S. fifteen. They had designed
a new baseplate, made of cast-iron and mild steel, which had
no serrations on the bottom and would certainly test the
spike's holding power. And by August 1944 the L.M.S. was
arranging to install a "ganger's length" with spikes that would
include points and crossings. The spike had never been used
on these before in this country.

At the end of November Swinnerton of the L.M.S. escorted
a party of V.I.P.s from the Ministry of War Transport, including Colonel Sir Alan Mount, on a tour of various track
experiments. As a result, he said, "the prestige of the Elastic
Rail Spike has gone up considerably".

The Chief Engineers of the "big four" railway companies now understood, it appeared, that in the post-war era they would not be permitted to carry out renewal programmes that cost more than they had done before the war. Yet the cost of labour alone had soared so much since then, and besides there was a massive arrears of work. Some means of economising had, therefore, to be found, and a reduction in maintenance expenditure was essential. Such a reduction, it was thought, could be achieved by switching to flat-bottomed track. W. K. Wallace, the L.M.S.'s Chief Engineer, had already pronounced himself satisfied that the initial cost of flat-bottom was no higher than that of bull-head, and that flat-bottom undoubtedly required less maintenance.

It looked, then, as though all the railways would be putting down flat-bottomed track during 1945 and that they would want Elastic Rail Spikes.

The good relationship cultivated by Rawes with the Chief Engineers of the L.M.S. and the L.N.E.R., Bill Wallace and Jack Train, over some fifteen years was now bearing plenty of fruit. It seemed from what they said that in 1947 they might be in a position to "consider fairly increased trade", as Rawes was cautiously to record.

Train, apparently, was still experimenting with the A.5 Spike for use with chaired track, and on hearing this Rawes immediately did his best to head him off the idea. "It was felt", as he soberly reported at the next board meeting, "that it was not desirable for such experimental work to be undertaken until we have technical assistance of the type which Mr. Sanson could provide".

Until now the L.M.S. and L.N.E.R. had been making all the running. Suddenly the G.W.R. woke up to the fact that it was a little behind the times and came in requesting a tender for some 60,000 spikes. A little later they said their requirement was now 118,000. Nor did the S.R. intend to stay out of the act

any longer. In June 1945 there came from Bill Wallace, who was
Chairman of the Railway Executive Committee's own Engineering Committee, an estimate of the leading railway companies'
requirements for 1945. It was as follows:

L.M.S.	198,000
L.N.E.R.	165,500
G.W.R.	118,000
S.R.	109,000
Total	590,500

By 1946 test tracks were being operated by all four companies.
Increasingly the problem of matching the supply of spikes to
the demand was growing. George Turton, Platts in Sheffield
had valiantly tried to produce what it could these last few
years, but its principal concern during the war had been the
production of screws, shell discs and barbed wire entangle-
ments. From time to time Rawes would call in on the Permanent Way Department and reprimand San Oldfield, its
foreman. "Why aren't you doing *our* work?" he used to say,
expecting to see a steady flow of spikes. And Oldfield would
reply, "I have to slip 'em in when I can."

Now the time had come when it was vital to set up a special
plant for producing the spikes. Plans had been prepared for
doing this, but Government approval for such a technically
unnecessary project was unobtainable. But George Turton,
Platts had, throughout the war, leased a Government shadow
factory at Worksop in Nottinghamshire. So various people,
including Rawes and Captain Cowen, the Managing Director
of G.T.P., put their heads together, with the result that the
lease of the Worksop works was taken and a new company set
up, Elasteel Limited, jointly owned by G.T.P., the Elastic
Rail Spike Company and Bernuth, Lembcke Co., Inc. A home
had been found at last for the manufacturing plant. All that
was needed was the plant.

With the assistance of G.T.P. this requirement was met. But Sam Oldfield did not move over to Worksop. During the war he had been, in his own words, burning the candle at both ends. Not only had he joined the A.R.P. and the Home Guard, but he had also been putting in three shifts at a time, without a break. And weekends too. Once he had worked for twenty-seven weeks solid without any time off. Feeling more than a bit run down, he called on his doctor. "Pack it up!" he was ordered. "I've had several chaps in like you and now they're all dead." And so Oldfield retired at what was for him the tender age of sixty-three. But from the point of view of L. N. Rawes, he had just been released to start a new career, as will later be appreciated.

When the war ended, the lack of manufacturing facilities was one thing. The steel famine was another. And in any case, owing to its paltry requirements pre-war, the Elastic Rail Spike Company found itself at the back of the queue for such small rations as there were. In August 1943 a letter had been received from Turton, Platts. They saw "no reason why adequate supplies (of silico-manganese steel) should not be forthcoming for purposes such as spike manufacture, and seeing that the country's steel production has been so greatly increased in connection with the war effort, we should imagine there will be no difficulty in obtaining the necessary quantity . . . to meet your full requirements." The subsequent course of events had proved their optimism unwarranted.

By January 1944 their production of 5/8 in. section spikes for the L.N.E.R. and L.M.S. was at a halt. There simply was not any raw material. Nor was any expected for at least another month. True enough, their requirements on behalf of the ERS Company were covered by licences, but these did not necessarily help. Turton, Platts kept making strenuous efforts to sub-contract in an attempt to ease the situation, but could not find a suitable firm. In March 1944 they still thought they

12. Lancelot Newling Rawes, Managing Director of Elastic Rail Spike Co. Ltd., 1937–1946, and Chairman, 1940–1961.

1. Leopold Stewart Sanson, Managing Director of Elastic Rail Spike Co. Ltd., 1946–1970.

13. Per Pande-Rolfsen, inventor of the 'Pandrol' Rail Clip.

14. D. S. Currie, Chief Civil Engineer of British Railways' Scottish Region, driving the five millionth 'Pandrol' Rail Clip to be installed in the Scottish Region. Ceremony at Costain's factory at Newmains, Lanarkshire, November 13th 1972.
By courtesy of British Rail.

16. 'Pandrol' comes in for close scrutiny on the mini-length of specimen track outside the L. S. Sanson Development Centre, September 11th 1970. Included in the group are H. T. Astley (far left), L. T. Gardner (sixth from left in group standing), S. F. Spedding (seventh from left, standing).

15. The opening of the L. S. Sanson Development Centre at Claylands Forge by the Chief Civil Engineer of British Railways, A. Paterson, F.I.C.E., September 11th 1970. On the far left, H. T. Astley. Main group, left to right: A. Paterson, G. P. Davies, L. S. Sanson, T. P. Brown (fifth from left), S. F. Spedding (tenth from left), C. R. Parratt (twelfth from left).

"should have someone else making spikes not only to get them used to and interested in the job but so that they can find their own source for the silico manganese strip required in some different area from this..."

At the same time they pointed out that "out of the 70 tons for Period I", they had only so far been able to place 25 tons, and so had had to refer the job to the Ministry of Supply. Nor did the next twelve months bring much improvement. The steel shortage stopped production entirely on—unlucky day!—April 13th 1945. One way and another, supplies were pretty desultory. And, from the moment of its formation, the new Elasteel Ltd. found precisely the same difficulty. It was, in the autumn of 1946, being forced to circularise every potential supplier it could think of. On February 12th 1947 there were no steel stocks whatsoever at Worksop. Nor were there any at Wolverhampton, where Bayliss, Jones & Bayliss were now trying to help out with spike production.

April 5th brought forth an announcement from Mr. Attlee's cabinet. It had been decided to give priority in the allocation of steel supplies to certain industrial users, in a given order. Of the six classes of user listed, the fifth consisted of "freight loco-motives and railway wagons for the transport of coal, and steel rails for maintenance of railway tracks". Rail fastenings as such were not included.

Eventually the company solved its problems by importing steel in large quantities from the Continent. And of course the other major wartime shortage, that of labour, had by that time ceased to be a concern. Acute enough, nevertheless, it had previously been. In November 1943 Turton, Platts had written to the company: ... "bad as the labour situation is now, we expect it to be a good deal worse during the coming year as the man power demands from the services will not diminish. Even now we are unable to man our machines to capacity so it is not a bit of use even thinking about buying other machines

D

even if we were permitted to do so, that would only stand idle."

Just over a year later, it seemed, they had (for spike manufacture) "merely the minimum number of men and boys required to keep one shift going," so that if a single employee was absent there was an inevitable loss of output. New boys were, anyway, difficult to keep. But in March 1945 G.T.P. reported that they had succeeded in getting hold of five men "against an order of January 30th to the local Labour Exchange for twelve men and eighteen youths". They had agreed to give women a try but so far none had been sent forward. And of their five new men, they remarked, one was currently away sick.

That restrained enthusiasm for wanting to see what the ladies could do was soon rewarded. A letter dated April 13th the same year mentioned, in a list of workers obtained, "two girls—satisfactory (up to now) and are still with us, although they were not secured through the offices of the Labour Ministry . . ."

So much for the vicissitudes of war and its aftermath. Tenaciously, and ambitiously, the Elastic Rail Spike Company had survived, loaded as the dice so often were against it. The offices, and their occupants, got by during the blitz, except for the time when 117 Fenchurch Street had its windows blown in by a near miss. Colonel Sanson sailed home from India in the New Year of 1946, and by July was in full harness once more, having on February 27th been appointed Managing Director in his absence.

And there was a triumphant postscript. On January 1st 1948 the nationalisation of the railways in Britain came into effect. By 1949 British Railways had decided to settle for flat-bottomed track, and to go with it there were to be two standard rail fastenings. One of them was the Elastic Rail Spike.

World Conquest

A period of grim austerity was, for Britain, the immediate sequel to World War II. During 1947 controls and rationing got tougher than they had ever been while the struggle was going on. The nation was now fighting for its economic life, and was desperately in need of dollars. Government exhortations to business to devote itself totally to the export drive soon outdid the Hallelujah Chorus at the decibel level.

The Elastic Rail Spike Company, however, scarcely needed to listen. That slogan "Export or die" had been the pivot of its philosophy throughout the years of its existence and there was little danger that it would be dropped now.

The mid-November of 1946 found Rawes and Sanson boarding a Sunderland flying boat for the eight-day flight to Australia. Way back in 1939 the company had been asked about the possibility of manufacturing spikes in the Antipodes. The original query had come from Plumb (Australia) Pty. Ltd., a subsidiary of Australian Consolidated Industries Ltd. in Sydney. On July 30th 1946 the General Manager of A.C.I. Ltd., A. E. Smith, had called in at Fenchurch Street to take up the discussion at the point where it had been forcibly abandoned owing to the war. Plumb's had, it seemed, switched identity and was now Hytest Axe & Tool Pty. Ltd., and well equipped to manufacture just such a product as the Elastic Rail Spike.

On August 28th, what is more, a couple of emissaries from the New South Wales Government Railways had turned up in

London, hot on the trail of the spike. One of them was the Deputy Chief Engineer, Colonel K. A. Fraser, who had been responsible for building the Hawkesbury Bridge and much regretted that the spike had not been specified for its track. He had not been aware that the N.S.W.R. test tracks incorporating the spike were of 1940 vintage, but knew that they had not been a great success, having been installed and operated under adverse conditions. He was writing immediately to his Chief Engineer, Major General Fewtrell, asking for a new start to be made. But what he and his colleague, W. K. King, had come about now was a supply of spikes for the Sydney Underground.

So Christmas 1946 was a sunny one for Sanson and Rawes. They did a tour of inspection of the main railway outfits in Victoria and New South Wales, and quickly acquired a substantial order from Victorian Railways. But it was essential to get the spikes made in Australia, since the steel shortage prevented them from being supplied from home. The first requirement was, then, to find a reliable team of Australian associates. They sought the advice of a leading firm of accountants, Flack & Flack, an offshoot of Price Waterhouse. A number of possible companies was scrutinised. But Rawes was very particular. "What I am looking for", as he characteristically put it, "is honest men". Back he went to Flack & Flack.

It so happened that the senior partner in Flack & Flack, Harold Chancellor, was also Chairman of one of the companies run by a couple of go-ahead chaps named Tutt and Bryant, who were associated with Allis Chalmers, the heavy vehicle people. George Edward Bryant, mechanical engineer and Sydney University graduate, had set up Tutt-Bryant Pty. Ltd. as a construction equipment company during the war, in partnership with Leo Edward Tutt. Bryant was something of a fireball. Nor did his interests stop short at machinery. As a farmer he was to import the first herds of Brahman cattle into Australia and successfully raise the breed in Queensland. Tutt, also a cattle breeder, who eventually acquired large properties in New South Wales, was the company's driving force on the sales side.

Chancellor thought it would be a good idea for Rawes and Sanson to meet these two men. But it happened to be a Friday when this suggestion cropped up. Rawes assumed that on the Saturday Mr. Tutt and Mr. Bryant would, like so many of their fellow countrymen, be away aboard their yachts. That supposition proved incorrect. Both men were working on Saturday morning. They met in a bar. Huge beers were ordered. Just after they had sat down Rawes was called to the phone. When he returned he found that the Australians had paid for the drink. "Either you take your money back, or there's no more talk!" bellowed Rawes, who had firmly decided this was his round.

The ice was broken. And from that moment a warm friendship started to grow. Here were the men Rawes had been looking for. And, as it turned out, they were well able to handle both the manufacture and the marketing of the spike in Australia. A form of agreement was initialled with them, and the formation by Tutt-Bryant of a subsidiary company was discussed. In any case, they were going to make the spikes, at an agreed price, and the first order would be big enough to provide Sanson with costing information.

Rawes returned to London, but not before he and Sanson had visited Sir Colin Syme of Broken Hill Pty. Co. Ltd., the big steelmakers, to enquire about getting local supplies. They had also flown across to New Zealand for a quick look round. And Rawes had not neglected to fit in quite a few rounds of golf. He knew what a valuable place the links was if you wanted to meet up with the right people.

Back at home, he reported on his visit. . . . "Due primarily,

if not solely, to the high regard in which Mr. Sanson was held
by all concerned, they had been well received everywhere by
Chief Commissioners of Railways and by Chief Civil Engineers",
and also by Sir Harold Clapp, Director General of Australia's
Railways Standardisation Division. The meeting with the

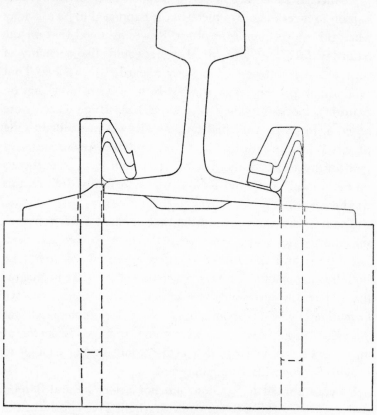

Fig. 2. Type T Elastic Rail Spikes with baseplates.

latter had been important, for the company had for some time
realised that the standardisation of gauge afforded an opportunity which would never come again. It was largely for this
reason that Australia at this moment was thought to present
London with its greatest marketing challenge.

Sanson stayed on for a while in the winter sun, selling to other railways, and buying large quantities of steel in order to alleviate the shortage in England. He negotiated with Essington-Lewis, Chairman of Broken Hill Pty. Co. Ltd., in connection with the plans for manufacture. Early in 1947 he was back in London and by May, the agreement with Tutt-Bryant formally settled, quotations were out with various railways. The Elastic Rail Spike Company (Australia) Pty. Ltd. had been set up on April 11th and Tutt-Bryant, armed with a licence to manufacture, were erecting a plant at Rydalmere, near Sydney. Delivery of 1,000 tons of steel was due to start in June. 50,000 A.1 Spikes were wanted by Victorian Railways.

By now the London company found it was getting orders in from Africa. One enquiry from the Crown Agents, for example, related to 20,000 SR.3 and 5,000 SR.9 Spikes for Uganda and Kenya. In this case permission was obtained to quote instead for 25,000 T.3 Spikes. And over in Malaya, Major John Mahony, Chief Engineer of the new Federated Malay States Railways, who had in June 1945 (before the defeat of the Japanese) announced his intention of using the spike for renewals, had asked for 50,000 T.4 and 540,000 T.7 Spikes. By 1947 Malayan Railways, as it now was, had become the first railway overseas to adopt the Elastic Rail Spike as standard. A test track which had been laid in that country before the war began was found, incidentally, after the Japanese departure, to have survived intact.

In India, late in 1945 Burn & Co. Ltd. of Howrah had made a few spikes which appeared to be satisfactory and were then arranging to turn out some 20,000 T.3 Spikes with the use of temporary plant. However, silico-manganese steel was unavailable in the sub-Continent, so they tried to buy from Australia. The agreement made with them never really resulted in anything, and by 1954 it was ended. 1945 had brought enquiries from the Great Indian Peninsular Railway, and in 1947 the Bengal-Nagpur Railway ordered 13,000 spikes.

The test track in Siam had less luck than that in Malaya. The company's agents in Bangkok wrote in December 1946 that "all records of the spike installation in the Siamese State Railways were destroyed by bombing in 1945."

Another problem area was South America, where the situation was confused by the fact that the New York company technically held the patents, although those for Brazil and Argentina had actually been confiscated by the U.S. Alien Property Custodian. Back in 1943 an enquiry about T type Spikes had come through from the Buenos Aires Great Southern Railway, whose earlier efforts to get spikes from Pittsburgh had failed "owing to the political situation". The company's agents in Buenos Aires, Percy Grant & Co., had a little later written:

"We anticipate substantial post-war orders of Elastic Spikes both from Buenos Aires Great Southern and Buenos Aires Western, and Central Argentine and the Central Uruguay will, we feel sure, order in accordance with their financial means."

In the spring of 1944 Percy Grant were trying to coax some 12,000 T type Spikes for the Central Uruguay Railway out of the New York firm. It was suggested that the request should be re-routed to London. By the following January both the Buenos Aires Great Southern and the Buenos Aires Western were asking for a few sample T Spikes to fit in the track "before placing the large post-war orders . . . which they have in mind". And by August 1945 there was a request from the Peruvian Corporation, on behalf of the Central Railway of Peru, for 10,000 SR.3 Spikes "as supplied 1938."

The indefatigable Buenos Aires Great Southern were back again by autumn 1945, now with the idea of a quarter of a million T type Spikes in their heads. Other enquirers by this time were the Central Argentine and the Chilean State. It was believed by Kenrick & Co., Percy Grant's *alter ego* agents in Chile, that the Chilean State Railways could be persuaded to standardise on the spike.

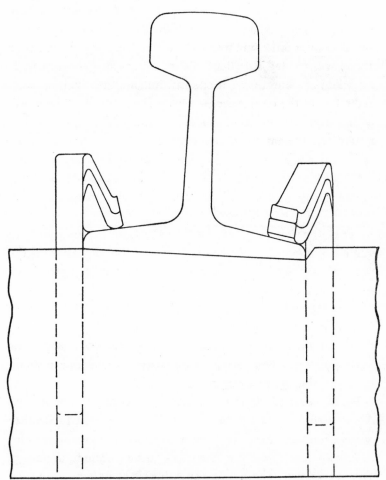

Fig. 3. Type T Elastic Rail Spikes without baseplates.

On December 14th 1945 a letter was sent to the Elastic Rail Spike Corporation in New York agreeing to pay them ½c per spike on all sales to any part of the South American continent. Twelve months later the board was told about an enquiry from Peru's Corporacion del Santa, which wanted 300,000 spikes for its Chimbote/Huallanca Railway. A quotation for 100,000 T.3 Spikes was given.

In Argentina, 70% of the railway network was British-owned, which perhaps made selling the spike a little easier. But this situation came to an abrupt end in 1947. When Juan Perón was elected President of the country in February 1946, he made it clear that nationalism and industrialisation were to be two of the cornerstones of his policy. And that the power of the state was to be supreme. So, inevitably, he decided to nationalise the railways. However, unlike other heads of state at later dates, he did not simply seize them. Instead he negotiated, and bought. And the price of £150 million he paid was regarded by many as generous. A body representing the various British-owned railway companies was set up, under the name of the British-Argentine Railway Council, and on April 22nd it announced that the question of the allocation of the proceeds among holders of loan and share capital would be referred to an independent panel.

The picture had entirely changed. Yet early in May 1947 the Elastic Rail Spike Company heard that its offer to supply 6,000 T type Spikes had been accepted by the new Argentine State Railways. The particular quantity may have been small, but its significance was great.

Early in 1948 Stewart Sanson was heading for Buenos Aires, eager to pick up the threads he had intended to gather on that long ago cancelled trip of September 1939. Eager also to renew contact with engineers he had met while in the army. Ten years were to go by, however, before an attempt could be made to consolidate the company's position in Argentina and a move made towards local manufacture.

The year 1949 was not very old when out of the blue came a frantic plea from the Chief Engineer of Australia's Victorian Railways. "Where are the spikes?" he was exclaiming. Sanson lost little time in packing his bags. He arrived on the other side of the world unheralded and unexpected. The problem was, he was told, that there just was not any steel. Round he went to see the management at Broken Hill Pty. Co. Ltd. He saw Essington-Lewis again, and was promised enough steel for a start to be made. The Elastic Rail Spike Company (Australia) Pty. Ltd. naturally enough, being new, had no record as a steel user, and therefore had no standing with regard to allocations.

Because of the steel shortage, production did not get into its stride until the middle of 1950, and on September 15th of that year the original licensing agreement between Tutt-Bryant and London was scrapped and in its place a supplementary agreement substituted between the Elastic Rail Spike Company and its Australian associate. The latter bought up all the existing plant, materials and stores at Rydalmere, near Sydney, and took over the manufacturing in rented premises there. Managing the Australian company now was C. R. Colville, an ex-New South Wales Railways engineer who had joined Tutt-Bryant in November 1948 and rapidly become involved in the setting up of the initial spike manufacturing plant. One of his jobs had been to induce Broken Hill Pty. Co. Ltd. to undertake the rolling of the first tonnage of steel Tutt-Bryant had received.

In July 1951 the young company removed itself to a leased site at Hornsby, New South Wales, where the plant was reinstalled. But far from being severed, the links with Tutt-Bryant were as strong as before. The controlling interest in the ERS Company (Australia) was owned by Tutt-Bryant's two principals (and from 1960 by L. Tutt & Company Pty. Ltd., a family company they formed), while the ERS Company in London held one-third of the shares. And G. E. Bryant was the Chairman.

To help get the new plant going, Sanson decided to enlist

the services of Sam Oldfield, with whom he and Rawes had not lost touch. Would he be willing to go to Australia? Well, yes, he would. So he went, to stay for almost two years. On the way out from Prestwick, the plane had engine trouble, and the passengers came in for an unplanned 24-hour stopover in Iceland. As soon as he arrived at Hornsby, Oldfield realised something was wrong. Intuitively he knew the spikes were just not up to scratch. He arranged for all the usual tests to be tried. But none of them gave a hint that anything was amiss. So Oldfield said, "Let's see the firm making the steel".

True to form, the Sheffield man had put his finger on it. The manufacturers, it appeared, made silico-manganese steel of two different kinds. One specification resulted in low carbon steel, the other in high carbon. And of these two classes of steel, it was clear that one must have been cheaper to produce than the other. What the makers did was to mix the two kinds together. This meant that uniform results were impossible. What they had to do, said Oldfield, was halve the specification and keep within a particular carbon range. His advice was taken, and after that there was no more trouble.

But to his critical eye, there were also other faults which needed putting right. The heating furnace was out of date, and the flames were reaching the steel. An expenditure of some £8,000 was required to fix that. The tempering furnace, too, had to be replaced. Oldfield and Colville did not always see eye to eye. But Sanson had said to the Yorkshireman, "What you say goes!" and Oldfield was determined that was the way things would be.

Sanson was to pay eighteen visits all told to Australia. Naturally he saw quite a lot of Tutt and Bryant. He must have seen a good deal of Bryant's attractive secretary besides. For it was not long before he had married her and carried her back with him to England.

By May 3rd 1960 an offshoot of the Australian company had

established itself at Midland Junction, near Perth in Western Australia. This was the ERS Company (Western Australia) Pty. Ltd. which operated for five years under an agreement with the Western Australia Government. When, at the insistence of the Commonwealth Government, dogspikes were adopted as standard for the upgrading of the Kalgoorlie-Perth line to standard gauge, the demand for Elastic Rail Spikes waned. So the new plant was closed and its equipment, fully bricked tempering and preheating furnaces included, transferred 2,500 miles back to New South Wales. It went not to Hornsby but to Seven Hills, a freehold site to which the main company had moved in March 1965. The Hornsby plant had become too small, there had been no room to expand, and because of the residential area close by afternoon and night shift work could not be carried out.

The Australian company's territory now took in New Zealand and Indonesia plus—from late 1964—the Philippines. Within the Commonwealth itself, Elastic Rail Spikes were soon digging themselves in on railways not only in Victoria (where that very first order had come from) and in Western Australia but also in Queensland, New South Wales, South Australia and Tasmania and on the Commonwealth Railway. Heaviest users of the spikes were to be Queensland and Western Australia which would take millions for laying directly upon timber sleepers. In Tasmania spikes were to be used to secure the Launceston-Bell Bay line which was to open to traffic in 1973.

The company owed much of its success to the energetic efforts of its first Chairman, G. E. Bryant, who was to die in September 1972 at the age of seventy-one. His successor in the chair was to be Leo Tutt. The real driving force, however, was and still is Ray Colville who is now Managing Director.

Meanwhile, in South Africa, the spike had been creating interest. South African Railways had sent two envoys, J. G.

Hay and A. Goldstein, to Europe in the summer of 1952 to check up on new developments in railway engineering. The idea of a resilient rail fastening had quickly claimed them as converts, and upon their return home invitations had been issued to those interested to submit offers for fastenings to be used in test tracks. In the subsequent trial the Elastic Rail Spike—used with timber sleepers—did very well for itself, and the result was that South African Railways requested a tender for one and a half million spikes.

This was early in 1957. Sanson had been in Johannesburg late in the previous year, investigating possibilities of local manufacture in the event of future orders, and keeping an eye on the spike trials, arrangements for which had been carried out by the company's agents, Sturrock (South Africa) Ltd. When he heard of the tender which had been asked for, he hurriedly returned to help in preparing it. When this was submitted, it incorporated a statement to the effect that, should an order be placed, a spike manufacturing plant would be set up in the Johannesburg area, together with a galvanizing plant, in order to cope with it. The invitation to tender stipulated that the spikes were to be galvanized, and in this respect South African Railways were following the lead of British Railways who, after adopting Elastic Rail Spikes as standard in 1949, had laid down the same requirement. Existing galvanizing facilities were, it was discovered, inadequate in the Rand.

So out to Africa with Sanson came Peter Wedge, Managing Director of the Worksop Galvanizing Co. Ltd., then an associate company of the ERS Co. Ltd. which had been formed in 1950. If the tender came off, it was decided, two local companies were to be set up, with the galvanizing outfit as a wholly-owned subsidiary of the spike company.

On the flight to South Africa, incidentally, Sanson and Wedge found that among their fellow passengers was an arch-competitor, with whom they were soon on socially friendly terms. During the stopover at Nairobi, this "third man" spotted a train away in the distance. "For God's sake don't let Stewart Sanson see that," he exclaimed, "or he'll want to go and see if they've got Elastic Rail Spikes in the track".

Together with Ernest Gearing, Joint Managing Director of Sturrock & Robson Holdings Ltd. (parent company of Sturrock [South Africa] Ltd.), Sanson went to see the Chief Civil Engineer of South African Railways. This was Goldstein, one of the pair which had been on that European reconnaissance five years back. "You build the factory," he said. "We will keep it busy."

On the strength of that official albeit off the cuff encouragement, and of the order itself when it came (shrunken though it now was to a mere 600,000 spikes), three acres of land were bought at Isando, an industrial suburb some fifteen miles out of Johannesburg. Plant and equipment were ordered, and factory buildings put up. And the Elastic Rail Spike Company (Pty.) Ltd., manufacturers of resilient rail fastenings, came into being, 60% of the shares being held by Sturrock (South Africa) Ltd. ,20% by B. E. Wedge Ltd. (Peter Wedge's own galvanizing firm in Staffordshire), and 20% by the ERS Company in London. The subsidiary company was called Isando General Galvanizers (Pty.) Ltd. The manager in overall charge of both plants was J. A. McCallum.

Ernest Gearing, meanwhile, hurried over to England to spend a couple of weeks at Peter Wedge's Willenhall galvanizing plant. Determined to learn the ropes fast, he rolled up his sleeves and worked shifts on the shop floor, much to everyone's admiration.

When the spike manufacturing plant was being started up, once again Sanson called on his veteran troubleshooter to come and give a hand. Sam Oldfield was now a sprightly seventy-three, yet only too delighted to have another go in pastures

new. He stayed for ten months or so, during which time he
established the best of relationships with the plant's black
machine operatives. The called him "the little boss".

One day a streak of lightning homed in on the steel in the
spike shop and the works was aswirl in three feet of water. But
that was nothing to what happened one week-end somewhere
between Johannesburg and Skukuza, on the edge of the Kruger
National Park. Jim McCallum, ex-R.A.F. pilot and a flying
enthusiast, offered to fly Sam and Bert Davie (the Scots foreman at the plant) to a farm up-country on condition that
they then drove a truck back to Isando. On the way back, it
rained. The truck was bogged down. Davie walked off to seek
help, while Sam settled down for the night. In the words of the *Star*,
a Johannesburg newspaper, "he heard some strange grunts in
the bush and thought they were cows". Next morning, within
fifteen yards, he noticed the remains of a freshly killed wilde-
beeste. Lion had been at the kill. Davie, who crazily had
walked six miles to the nearest store, enlisted help. McCallum
flew back to the rescue, and Sam agreed he "had seen enough" of
the South African countryside.

That initial order for 600,000 T.3 Spikes was supplied. But
it quickly became obvious that, in spite of the encouraging
noises which had been made, South African Railways would
not be looking for any more spikes. The main reason was that
the exceptionally dry South African climate exaggerated, it
was felt, the tendency of the very hard timber used for sleepers
to split when spikes were driven into it. In any case, supplies
of wooden sleepers were becoming scarce. Another contri-
butory factor, perhaps, was the fact that both McCallum,
whose interest was largely focussed on the galvanizing activity,
and his successor J. Hyslop were essentially production engineers. What the new company needed now was a marketing man
to guide its fortunes. He was found in the person of W. G. S.
Barnett, who took over in 1960.

17. A view of the 'Pandrol' Rail Clip assembly line. Clips shown falling on to cooling belt.

18. A view of the Amsler Test Rig with a rail section secured by 'Pandrol' Rail Clips being tested.

19.   Proving ring at Claylands Forge, proving the load of a 'Pandrol' Rail Clip.

Walter Barnett had put in a substantial stint selling engineering equipment to the mines in South Africa, and he was quick to realise that in that field the T.10 Spike might well find a valuable market. He got on to London for details of that spike and, finding that it required a lighter steel section, arranged for a quantity of this to be rolled in a small privately owned rolling mill. A mountain of problems now started piling up. The technical staff at the mill seemed quite unable to roll the thin steel section that was called for. However, the mill was owned by a Portuguese who, although not an engineer at all, possessed an unusual amount of determination. Taking over the operation of the mill himself for almost forty-eight hours nonstop, he succeeded in accomplishing the task which had defeated his experts. From then on the section was successfully and economically rolled, according to a regular schedule, and supplied to the ERS Company (Pty) Ltd.

At last the T.10 Spikes could be made. Soon they were being offered on a free trial basis to a number of the larger gold mines and in particular to prominent mining engineers. And they sold themselves. The market the company needed had been found, and even after the original patent for the Elastic Rail Spike had expired and an imitative competitor had moved in, it was to remain a substantial one. Today the company is still the principal supplier of spikes to the entire South African mining industry.

After having galvanized that initial order for 600,000 spikes, Isando General Galvanizers also had to hunt around for work. Under Barnett's able and enthusiastic direction they polished up their techniques and trimmed their costs, and moved into the attack on the general galvanizing front, taking on steel plate, baskets for milk bottles, everything. During the next few years a serious rival was eliminated, and the company grew into the biggest and best known galvanizing set-up in the country, with Rhodesia, Malawi and Mozambique included

E

in its territory. Recently it parted from the ERS Company Group, having been disposed of so that the parent company could expand its operations on the land occupied by I.G.G.'s plant.

Ernest Gearing was appointed Managing Director of the ERS Company (Pty.) Ltd. at the time its struggle for survival began. His contribution to the success which has been achieved has been very considerable, and his able hand remains at the helm. Swaziland was added to the company's territory in 1960, together with Lesotho (Basutoland as it then was), as a result of reports that the British Government was contemplating building a railway through these countries to Mozambique. Malawi was also added in 1967, and so was the Trans-Zambesia Railway. During 1959 valuable assistance was given to the company by W. K. Wallace, who had joined the board of the ERS Co. Ltd. in London in February 1957, and who visited not only Johannesburg but also Salisbury and Bulawayo to discuss the marketing of the spike with South African Railways and Rhodesia Railways.

Across the South Atlantic, in Brazil, a company was formed to protect the name of the Elastic Rail Spike in 1960. It rejoiced in the title of Elastic Rail Spike—Indústria e Comércio de Grampos Elásticos para Trilhos Ltda. An agreement had been entered into earlier—in the autumn of 1958—with a firm in São Paulo, Molas Scripelliti S.A., manufacturers of springs for Mercedes and Volkswagen cars, allowing it to make spikes for sale in Brazil. The start-up of the spike producing plant had been another Sam Oldfield operation. Oldfield had spent some six months in São Paulo supervising the installation of the furnaces and in general "simply showing 'em how to do it". No encounters with lion this time. Instead he watched the legendary Pele play for Santos, and took a fancy to the Japanese flower arrangements which he came across at an exhibition.

So in Brazil the normal pattern was broken. You had an

outside firm doing the manufacture, while the home company's own subsidiary performed the marketing function only.

Sam Oldfield retired—for the second time, but this was final—on April 30th 1960. By then he had fitted in yet another major turnkey job, this time in Europe. In July 1956 an agreement had been fixed with Simmel Industrie Meccaniche S.p.A., of Castelfranco Veneto, some thirty miles north-west of Venice, with a view to the manufacture of spikes in Italy and their sale in Italy and Jugoslavia. Sam paid two or three visits to the virgin plant, and designed the tools that were to be used. Yet, when the first spikes came rattling off the production line, he knew in his uncanny way that something was wrong with them. He could tell just by looking. "They're no bloody good!" rasped that Yorkshire voice. Tests carried out on the new and sophisticated hardness testing machine revealed no fault, but Sam was insistent. The machine itself was sent for test and found to be wrongly calibrated. Sam's nose for trouble had not let him down. The sequel? Sucessful production in Italy as from 1961.

The 1956 agreement with regard to Italy had been followed nine months later by another relating to the manufacture of the spike in Austria. This one was arranged with a company by the name of Schoeller-Bleckmann Stahlwerke Aktiengesellschaft, of Viennese provenance, and bore in mind possible future sales not only in Austria but also in a galaxy of iron curtain countries, namely Bulgaria, Czechoslovakia, the German Democratic Republic, Hungary, Poland, Rumania and the U.S.S.R. From the marketing point of view, Europe was not by any means new territory. An order for 150,000 T.4 Spikes had come in from the Swiss Federal Railways in mid-1947, for example. On the Continent things were, in general, going well, although progress in France had been something of a disappointment.

Late in 1946 the S.N.C.F. (Société Nationale des Chemins

de fer Français) had said it wanted 30,000 T.3 Spikes for use without an intermediary baseplate. The answer then had been that, owing to the supply problem in Britain, the ERS Company thought it best that a firm should be found in France to make the spikes under a royalty arrangement. It seemed that no spikes had so far been installed in France, although the S.N.C.F. was thinking of testing the A and T types. The real problem was that, according to the company's agent in France, Etienne Querné, many people felt the Continent was an area "reserved to German manufacturers of Elastic Rail Spikes", the original inventor Max Rüping having retained just the one patent for Germany which could now be interpreted as being in force in adjoining countries. So in this particular direction a kind of impasse seemed to have been reached.

Nor were there any development in the United States. Orders for spikes had been placed, but the London company had no sales rights there, while the sister organisation in New York had by this time disappeared from the scene. Argentina was another matter. Sanson went there in 1959 and the outcome of his visit was the decision to set up an associate company to be known as Elastic Rail Spike (Argentina) S.A. The parent company would subscribe up to £20,000 towards its share capital. Early in 1962 the Argentine company was asking for additional capital, but London felt averse to increasing its investment in Argentina when extra funds could probably be found locally. As indeed they then were. A small plant had been started in a suburb of Buenos Aires, and from Worksop someone had been sent out to 'do an Oldfield' and help get it going. This was Doug Best, who spent four months in 1962 supervising the installation of the Argentine-built machines and furnace equipment. The initial tooling had been supplied from Britain.

The practical difficulties here were enormous, and they were largely caused by the continual devaluation of the peso.

Business as such was good, but its rewards could not be translated into dividends. Devaluation had reduced the value of the London company's peso shares by over £10,000 in May 1965, and by February 1967 the total investment was worth only £6,700, the exchange rate now being 685 pesos to £1 as against 480 to £1 in May 1965. September 1967 saw the total investment being written down to a mere £4,700. This represented 41.2% of ERS (Argentina) S.A.'s share capital.

Furthermore, although spikes were sold, it was not always easy to get payment for them. One customer, in fact, had to be taken to court. Yet in Argentina there were some 27,000 miles of railway, far more than any other Latin American country could muster. Whatever the problems, such a market could not be neglected. So the struggle continued, being waged with increasing success by Richard Delacroix, the able local manager and partner.

In Africa, the Elastic Rail Spike had been specified for the Cubal Variant project of Angola's Benguela Railway, which involved the straightening of the line to reduce mileage. And here stern competition had been encountered from a French rail fastening. The consumption of spikes continued, meanwhile, in Nigeria, where it seemed there were several spike addicts. One of them, who initiated orders from time to time, was a man who had started as a junior engineer on Nigeria's railway system back in 1947, after war service with the Royal Engineers and the Bombay Sappers and Miners, and had by 1960 become Deputy Chief Engineer. His name was Trevor Astley. Another was a Welshman named A. I. Webber Jones, Chief Engineer of Nigerian Railways up to 1961, which was the year both he and Astley joined the Elastic Rail Spike Company instead. And a third was the Chief Engineer's Permanent Way Assistant, W. G. Houghton, who had served his track apprenticeship on the Southern Railway.

Houghton came to London in 1957 and saw Rawes. "You'll be no good to us, you know, for a long time", said the Chairman. "You've no commercial experience." But W.G.H. was not dismayed. Before long he had become one of the company's most valued roving ambassadors.

In Asia, the spike was going well. Ceylon was a good customer, and so was Burma. November 1967 saw a tender being sealed for 340,000 spikes, asked for by Rangoon's Myanma Export Import Corporation. In Malaya, where there had been talk of manufacture back in 1961, competition started building up from a German spike, yet in spite of this 50% of the market was retained. By now, of course, the original patents for the Elastic Rail Spike had expired. So the field was open to all comers. Yet although opposition was certainly not lacking, the first of the resilient spikes held its own.

A consignment of Elastic Rail Spikes even found its way to a location overseas where no railway either has existed or is ever likely to do so. When the people of Tristan da Cunha returned home in 1963 after their temporary exile in Britain, a slipway was constructed on the island. It consisted of a couple of rails, for which not surprisingly fastenings were needed.

The Factory at the Forge

"Where now are the bones of Wayland the wise, that gold-smith so glorious of yore . . .?" wrote an Anglo-Saxon poet more than a thousand years ago. Wayland was the magical smith, "the supreme craftsman" of old England, who made swords and armour fit for heroes. If you left your horse at Wayland's forge, "with a sixpenny fee, and went away for a short time—the smith not wishing to be watched while at work"—you would find your steed fully shod when you got back.

It is true there is no evidence to show that Claylands Forge is a corruption of Wayland's. A less romantic explanation of the name was suggested in a directory of 1832 which simply said that "the clay found here made fine bricks", and doubtless this is the prosaic but real derivation. Yet in Saxon times Wayland Smith was every bit as familiar and admired as Robin Hood was later to become. It is difficult to resist twisting the tail of historical fact and claiming him as the patron and guardian spirit of twentieth century Worksop's factory at the forge.

There was indeed a forge department in the original shadow factory built for the Ministry of Aircraft Production during the early days of World War II. This factory was leased by the Ministry to George Turton, Platts & Co. Ltd. who started manufacturing air-cooled aero engine cylinders both here and at their main works in Sheffield, using a forging and rough machining process. The forging equipment consisted of 1,000-ton hydraulic presses specifically designed for piercing and extrusion work. Cylinders were turned out in considerable quantities for the Armstrong Siddeley Cheetah and the Napier Sabre engines.

The work force consisted of a horde of Workshop women and young girls plus a skeleton corps of electricians, fitters and tool setters and the men running the heat treatment department.

As the war growled its way through the early nineteen-forties, Turton, Platts somehow managed to fit in Elastic Rail Spike manufacture, on a very modest scale, along with their military work. This was at Meadowhall Road in Sheffield. In 1943 they were arranging for the shaping of the spikes to be done by sub-contractors, while they were themselves to do the rest of the manufacturing process. By August of that year, despite a spot of bother with an oil cooler, they were producing 7,000 A.1 Spikes a week, and hoping to have their order for 81,000 completed by mid-November. And 100,000 SR.8 Spikes were more or less promised by about the same date, these being for export to Katanga.

But there was little hope of increasing production. Labour was scarce. In any case, the firm's Permanent Way Department had a prior commitment which involved the manufacture of steel rail keys (for the bull-headed track of the day). And there was the continuous steel shortage to cope with. Changes were made in the lay-out of the plant to help save labour, and by April 1944 new tools were at work and performing well. Production stopped altogether for some three weeks while further alterations were made. There was a Yorkshire coal strike which affected the gas supply.

Returning from a visit to Sheffield at the end of April, Betty Buckingham—secretary to Rawes and virtually his right hand —reported that Turton, Platts were "contending with really tremendous difficulties on account of all aspects of the labour situation". By August, all the same, progress was being made. There were two production units in action, one making

A type and the other T type Spikes, and 10,000 SR.8 Spikes were to be made each month "with machinery otherwise employed for aircraft work".

Two months later Captain J. C. Cowen, Managing Director of Turton, Platts, was saying that he did not wish their "present seeming inability to increase production" to impede the ERS Company's expanding business, and suggested there was room for "an independent second-string producer". But by the time serious negotiations had begun with a firm in Sunderland, the war was over, at least in Europe.

The moment had arrived for an entirely new plant to be started up, a plant devoted exclusively to the manufacture of Elastic Rail Spikes. The site was by now obvious enough—Claylands Forge, of course. It was not immediately available, but it soon enough would be. The first move was to form a company to run it, and on August 13th 1945 Elasteel Limited was incorporated. The initial share capital amounted to £10,000. Half the shares were paid up by George Turton, Platts, one quarter by the Elastic Rail Spike Company, and one quarter by Bernuth, Lembcke Co., Inc. of New York. At the first directors' meeting, held at 420 Meadowhall Road, Wincobank, Sheffield on September 19th, Rawes and W. H. Newson represented the ERS Company interest, and Captain Cowen and Frank Hewitt that of G.T.P. Rawes was elected Chairman, while Cowen was appointed Managing Director.

The Claylands Forge factory had not quite changed landlords. But the Ministry of Aircraft Production was only half in the picture, for the Board of Trade (Control of Factory Premises) now held the site for disposal. The civil servants in this department were at once subjected to a sustained bombardment of letters, telephone calls and personal visits, as a result of which everything was by November more or less lined up for Elasteel Ltd. to take over at Worksop during the following month. The idea was that while for the time being production would continue at Sheffield in the G.T.P. works, some plant would be moved over to Claylands Forge so that a start could be made before fresh machines and equipment were installed there.

That army of ladies had already dispersed. Six men only were left to dismantle the wartime machinery and pack it off to the Ministry of Supply's disposal centre at Ruddington. Three were labourers, three were fitters. In command was G.T.P.'s Doug Best, who had originally been one of Sam Oldfield's lads in Sheffield.

For a short while the factory at the forge was empty. Until, that is, two surplus presses were shipped in from Sheffield. Best remained, to join Elasteel Ltd. Or, as he put it, for Elasteel to join him. A couple of new furnaces were on the way. G.T.P.'s application for a new lease on a peacetime footing had been accepted by the Ministry of Aircraft Production, and to begin with they planned to let Elasteel Ltd. take over the machine shop on a sub-lease.

But the leasing negotiations inevitably had to move at a civil servant's pace, and it was over three years before the matter was finally ironed out. The Government department concerned was now the Ministry of Supply, with whom G.T.P. reached an agreement by May 1947. The lease was for ten years as from September 1st 1946, and the annual rental was to be £1,575, subject to revision after five years. This was legalised on January 13th 1949, and it was not until the following June 14th that Elasteel Ltd. was able to affix its company seal to the Under-Lease.

The plant took time to install and get going. And the men had to be trained, for the trade was entirely new to the district. By September 1946 four units, each consisting of two presses and a furnace, were in production, although during October lack of steel caused a shut-down lasting almost a week. Monthly production was up to 207,900 spikes that December, and "one new man working on the single furnace unit produced 2,976 spikes in one day of 8 hours 50 minutes working time, which equals an output of 337 spikes per hour".

Six units were in action by May 1947, but the labour force was too big for the output being achieved. Spring steel was in such short supply, and the factory's production capacity was already considerably over and above what it was able to produce. However, two more units had been added by September 1948, and each unit was then turning out a thousand spikes every three hours of the working day.

During the twelve months up to August 1949 Claylands Forge produced 5,557,000 spikes, or practically 90% more than the amount the previous year. Some 3,700 tons of steel bar had been obtained, and things were certainly looking brighter.

Elasteel Ltd. was now a "fifty-fifty" company. Bernuth, Lembcke Co., Inc. of New York had sold its shares to the ERS Company in March 1949, so that the latter now held one half of the total shares and G.T.P. the other. Some spikes were still being produced by G.T.P. in Sheffield, where since Sam Oldfield's retirement the Foreman of the Permanent Way Department had been Eli Penn.

By this time there were some fifty people employed at Claylands Forge in the manufacture of spikes, under Works Manager Ben Gott. There was also a small establishment of feathered occupants of the factory. In 1949, after all, there were still ration books and eggs were hard to come by. So when a young man named Ron Parratt arrived at the gate one day in answer to an advertisement for a temporary cost accountant, the first thing he saw was a rabble of clucking hens accompanied by a man in a straw hat. It appeared that "Straw-hat" was in fact the night watchman. One of his duties was to keep an eye on the poultry in which the Works Manager and others had invested in order to alleviate their own personal food shortage.

Parratt was taken on. Shortly before Christmas he observed

that four geese had been added to the works staff. And it came to his ears that the night watchman, anxious about the danger of pilfering, had persuaded management to let him bring a dog along to help him guard the premises. By way of consideration for this he was being paid a few extra bob. Precisely two days before Christmas, however, the four geese vanished. No telltale feathers were to be found. Nor, oddly enough, had any barking been heard from the new guard dog. Clearly that quartet of expensive birds had found its way to the wrong dinner tables, notwithstanding the fact that the dog's allowance had only just been negotiated.

But there was an even sadder story. The works cat decided one day to have its litter in one of the furnaces. The kittens perished before this discovery had been made, although their parent escaped with a singe or two and lived on at Claylands Forge for many a day.

The April of 1950 found the plant producing roughly 4,000 spikes per unit every working day, and steel supplies had improved to such an extent that they were now being limited and the stockpile was being worked down to a manageable size. About one third of the steel received during the preceding year had come from Austria. Yet, such were the ups and downs of the steel situation that by November 1951 production was down to four days a week, and was to stay that way for a good four months or so.

A switch was made from gas to oil-firing. Two more production units were installed, and the factory's capacity went up by 14%. The daily spike output stood at around 40,000 by mid-1955, and there was now storage room for 1,000 tons of steel bar and a million spikes. At the end of that year Ben Gott retired and was succeeded as Works Manager by P. W. Davies, who was appointed to the board a few months later as an additional representative of the G.T.P. interest, Captain Cowen having been ill for some time.

Before long production was soaring to a record-breaking level. During the year up to July 31st 1958, 20 million spikes were manufactured, and this period was to be referred to from then on as "Twenty Million Year". Orders were pouring in, and on the dot delivery was being maintained. Complaints from customers, about either quality or delivery, were virtually non-existent. The standard of quality control was extraordinarily high. No other company anywhere could match the service provided on the manufacturing side by Elasteel Ltd. and in the marketing sense by the ERS Company itself.

One of the principal reasons for the Group's success was then, as it would continue to be, its original approach to management and to marketing. Other manufacturers of rail fastenings, for example, sold them by weight. Not so the ERS Company. The spikes were counted out before being put into bags, so that every customer knew precisely how many of them he was getting. Approximate figures were not enough.

Sanson's drive and vision were not limited either to the technical area or to salesmanship. He applied himself to the entire field of the Group's activities, and was for ever developing fresh ways of solving specific problems—ways which he habitually encapsulated in theoretical directives which might well have been dubbed "Sanson's Laws". One such dictum was that "the man who controls sales must control production if he is to give accurate sales forecasts". Naturally, this was put into practice, and particularly in relation to steel. It was laid down that the steel for Elasteel Ltd. should be bought in London, which was where the point of sale was. Later on, the steel for Torque Tension—the subsidiary company which would be producing mining roof bolts—was to be bought from Worksop, since in that case the product's point of sale was the same as the point of manufacture.

What happens today is that Elasteel Ltd. presents London with its production programme for three months, and the amount of steel required is then deduced from this. Purchases are planned accordingly.

But in the early days problems were not solved over night. There was that noxious fog of oil vapour, for instance, that used to rise from the open quench tanks. And there were those unpredictable fluctuations in output caused by the erratic supply of steel. There were also problems which arose from differences of opinion over policy. The G.T.P. representatives on the board of Elasteel Ltd. did not always see eye to eye with those from the ERS Company. Sometimes there were fairly fierce clashes. The advent of a new fastening, the 'Lockspike' Baseplate Fastening, led to one.

Production of this was initially carried out by G.T.P. at Sheffield. But it was agreed that space needed to be found for additional production at Claylands Forge, or if not there somewhere else. Captain Cowen did not like the thought of the Lockspike being manufactured alongside the Elastic Rail Spike, on the same site. Frank Hewitt, Joint Managing Director of G.T.P., categorically wanted to see Lockspike production staying in Sheffield. But Sanson took the opposite view. Manufacture at Worksop would, he claimed, overcome two major difficulties, namely uncertainty as to what production costs really were, and irregularity of supplies. It would also afford protection for Elasteel Ltd.'s employees through the introduction of an alternative and still patented product. As to the question of possible "labour friction", which Cowen had raised, all he could say was that Lockspikes and Elastic Rail Spikes were already being produced in Australia side by side at the same plant.

The lease of Claylands Forge expired on November 30th 1955. The problem that then arose hinged upon the desirability or otherwise of bidding for the freehold of the site. Eventually another lease was decided upon, and this was obtained, for a period of twenty-one years, after a certain amount of bargaining about the rental. But it took until January 1958 before the negotiations were completed. And by this time the situation had changed a good deal. New buildings had been put up, and others were contemplated, on land that was leasehold. Yet nobody likes building on leasehold land. So it was decided that the outright purchase of Claylands Forge should be negotiated. Sanson was given the job. Some five months later, after battles with the Ministry of Supply, he was able to report that the deal had been settled. The sale was completed on December 3rd.

One day in April the previous year two new men had joined the Group at Worksop. H. M. Marshall, an ex-naval engineer, was to become General Manager of Workshop Galvanizing Co. Ltd., while S. F. Spedding—an ex-Royal Navy regular with a spell of power station engineering in Egypt under his belt—would eventually be Elasteel's Works Manager. At Claylands Forge, the second generation was moving in. Ron Parratt had stayed on to be Assistant Company Secretary, and on August 1st 1959 Len Gardner took over as his number one when Cyril Rodgers, a G.T.P. man, vacated the post. Doug Best, who had designed the second set of tooling for Elastic Rail Spike production at the plant, and invented a pressing machine for Lockspikes, was in charge of the fitting staff (and eventually to become Chief Inspecting Engineer).

Following the peak production season of 1957–58, it looked as though the immediate demand for spikes was likely to fall. For one thing, British Railways had apparently been over-ordering in the past and now therefore was cutting down its orders. Another reason was the damage done to the export market by various political upheavals overseas, and notably in Malaya and the Middle East. So, in view of the fact that the plant's productive capacity had in any case never been fully exploited, it was felt essential to find fresh work for the machines that would otherwise soon start to be idle. The manufacture of Lockspikes provided one answer. Experimental work in connection with the possible future production of the 'Pandrol' Rail Clip was also begun. By December 1958 the Assistant Managing Director, P. W. Davies, was being authorised to look into the question of new plant for manufacturing Pandrol Clips and being given a budget to buy it with.

At this stage differences of opinion between the two shareholders of Elasteel Ltd.—G.T.P. and the ERS Company— had grown rather than diminished. Matters were complicated by the fact that another firm, Samuel Osborn & Co. Ltd., had acquired a controlling interest in George Turton, Platts. (Osborn himself, incidentally, although a veteran of eighty, still drove himself to work in his Bentley and was at his desk at eight o'clock each morning.) The parting of the ways was inevitable. And by June 1959 the G.T.P. interest in Elasteel Ltd. had been bought out by the ERS Company. Captain Cowen was succeeded as Managing Director by L. S. Sanson, while P. W. Davies became Works Director and Sanson's deputy. And when Rawes retired in the August of 1961 Sanson also became Chairman.

Production was now about to receive a major setback. British Railways had found itself forced to reduce its orders of Elastic Rail Spikes two or three years earlier. When Dr. Beeching took over as Chairman of the British Transport Commission during 1961, one of the first things he did was to get someone to look into the stocking position with regard to every kind of component. An Australian named Philip Shirley was entrusted with this task. Beeching thought, wisely enough, that the supplier ought to carry the stocks, not the consumer. Sure enough, Shirley found that British Railways was overstocked with many components, and one of them was the Elastic Rail Spike. So at once requisitions were pared to the bone.

Clearly the company's export drive would have to be sustained more strenuously than ever. Moreover, in the case of such orders as British Railways did require, stern adherence to delivery dates would be vital if a profitable relationship was to continue with this most important of all customers. In this respect, the company never once failed.

Of course, a secret weapon was being developed. It was the 'Pandrol' Rail Clip. Production began in the Old Shop at Claylands Forge during June 1959, employing the same quench and tempering arrangements as those which had been devised for the original spike. Soon three forging furnaces were in commission. A new integrated production line came into use early in 1965, complete with its own forging and tempering furnaces, quench tank, oil coolers and cooling conveyors, to which dipping and bagging units were later added.

Largely in response to British Railways' requirement in 1966 for heavier clips, a second production line came into action in that year. The manufacture of baseplates for the 'Pandrol' Assembly was also undertaken with the assistance of a 250-ton press.

Inspections of the production lines were introduced early. A weekly visit by a British Railways inspector was instituted, and the Crown Agents felt free to send someone along whenever this was necessary in relation to a specific order. Inspections were being carried out on a continuous basis by the plant's own team, which consisted of five shop floor inspectors and four hardness checkers, the latter being responsible for keeping an eye, of course, on the quality of the steel.

Co-existing with Elasteel Ltd. on the 4.1-acre Claylands Forge site since way back in 1950 had been Worksop Galvanizing Co. Ltd. A third Group company moved in during 1968 in the shape of Torque Tension (UK) Ltd. (plain Torque Tension Ltd. as it was shortly to become). And it was on September 11th 1970 that a £50,000 research shop—a labora-

F

tory where the continuous quest for ways to improve could be pursued—was officially opened by the Chief Civil Engineer of British Railways, A. Paterson, F.I.C.E. Since the initiative for this had come from Sanson, it was appropriate that it should have been christened the L. S. Sanson Development Centre.

As in the case of raw material supply, design and development have always been interwoven with the sales function in London. In 1966 a young man named Trevor Brown joined the company after working for many years with J. C. Loach in the British Railways Board's Research Department (Permanent Way Section) at Derby. Since that time Trevor 'B' has been responsible to Trevor 'A'—Trevor Astley—for technical development of the companies' products. The widespread export markets sought by the company have meant that a probably unrivalled knowledge of railway practices and track material standards has been built up over the years. More than 1900 drawings, for example, have been prepared, the vast majority showing variations of the 'Pandrol' Rail Fastening Assembly concept applied to different rail sections and sleeper types.

At the beginning of 1967 Ron Parratt was appointed Elasteel Ltd.'s Works Director. Although by training a cost accountant, he rapidly mastered the engineering side too, and lost little time in striving to develop the most congenial possible relationship between management and the shop floor. "Employers", as he says, "have an obligation to improve the scene". When the factory's social club had been formed in 1950, Parratt had taken on the job of treasurer. Later he was to become its president, and an enthusiastic organiser of annual dinners and dances, family outings to the coast, children's parties, sports both indoor and outdoor, and of a club for the sick.

It became the rule that all operatives should be trained within the plant, and that there should be a recognised ladder of progress from the simpler to the more skilled jobs. In 1967 the conversion was begun of an office block to provide somewhere for the works employees to change and have a shower. Management subsidised the social club, and a canteen. Pension schemes, a retirement benefit and life assurance were introduced. Such things are what you would expect a large organisation to offer. But it is unusual to find them on tap in such a small works as Claylands Forge.

Once or twice improvements in working conditions have been impeded by a certain innate local conservatism, as for example when Parratt tried to turn Good Friday into a holiday, which in this part of the world it is not. Within minutes of his noticeboard announcement being put up, someone was in to complain. Why Good Friday? Couldn't it be changed? There was no race meeting on that day. The pubs were open only between twelve and two. And if you couldn't either drink or back the horses, what was the point? Parratt's bright idea was, after that, duly abandoned.

Tradition is pretty strong at Claylands Forge. It is common to find sons working alongside their fathers. And there is a sizeable contingent of employees who have been with the company for twenty-one years or more. Rail fastenings seem to run in the blood.

Lockspike and the Pandrol Revolution

Sanson and his team possessed in ample quantity that sense of urgency which had for a hundred years characterised British railway engineers. No sooner had the Elastic Rail Spike at last well and truly established itself than they were engaged in the hunt for its successor.

In 1949 a major battle had been won when British Railways opted for flat-bottomed track and picked the spike as one of its two standard fastenings. During the period immediately following that much effort was devoted to 'after sales service' in respect of the spikes British Railways already had taken. The intention was to increase the proportion of Elastic Rail Spikes in use as against the competitive fastening, which was the Macbeth Spike. The latter was particularly favoured in the Western Region, and perhaps this was not surprising, for it had originated in the West Country, an area linked since the days of Brunel with a highly individual approach to technological problems. Eventually the Elastic Rail Spike seemed to have secured some three-quarters of the market.

Yet, as Sanson could well see, the days of the spike were already in a sense numbered. There was little doubt that soon there would be a move to welded rails, and to concrete sleepers, for neither of which the spike would be suitable. Experiments had been going on with welded rails for years. For if only bolted rail joints could be eliminated, travel would be much smoother and quieter for one thing (no more of that "diddly-da, diddly-da"). There would be less wear and tear for the rolling stock; and track maintenance would be greatly reduced.

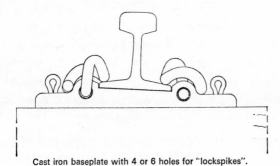

Cast iron baseplate with 4 or 6 holes for "lockspikes".

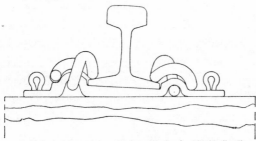

Rolled steel baseplate with 4 or 6 holes for "lockspikes".

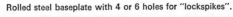

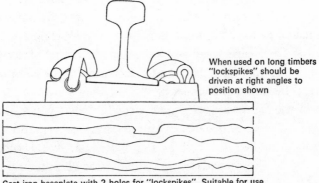

When used on long timbers
"lockspikes" should be
driven at right angles to
position shown

Cast iron baseplate with 2 holes for "lockspikes". Suitable for use
on open deck bridges or on longitudinal bridge timbers.

THE "PANDROL" RAIL FASTENING FOR WOOD SLEEPERS.

PANDROL LTD, 7 ROLLS BUILDINGS, LONDON, EC4. Dwg Nº 861.

Fig. 4.

Australia had its test length of welded track, near Sunderland in New South Wales, as early as the June of 1931, and by 1932 the New South Wales Railways had gone in for rails of this kind seriously. In the United States, welded rail was tried out in 1933 by the Delaware and Hudson Railroad, which during the next six years laid some thirty miles of it. By the 1950s American railways were in general becoming welded-minded. British Railways did not move in on the act until 1955 when it put down a mile of continuously welded track.

The move towards concrete sleepers took it original impetus from the shortage of timber. British Railways was using sleepers made of pre-stressed concrete even with some of its bull-head track, and by the early 'fifties the French and the Germans were installing them with flat-bottomed track, although the Americans were not to start their experiments until some ten years later. In due course British Railways was to be covering the country with giant 1200-foot continuous welded rails laid on concrete sleepers with a life expectation of fifty years.

So, by the time the twentieth century was itself fifty years old, a hectic season of new developments was fast setting in. And it looked as though one inevitable development would be a switch from direct rail fastenings (such as the Elastic Rail Spike), securing both rail and baseplate to the sleeper, to indirect fastenings. Independent fastenings had, of course, been in use for a very long time already. What you had were screwspikes fixing the baseplate to the sleeper, and other fastenings holding the rail to the baseplate. Early types of fastening of the second category had needed nuts and bolts to do the job, and since they tended to work loose in traffic conditions a great deal of regular maintenance was required.

A resilient indirect fastening was clearly what the ERS Company should now be thinking about. To begin with, a resilient independent fastening was found—in the shape of an

American invention, the Lockspike. At a board meeting held on August 24th 1950 it was reported "that Mr. Arthur Corbus Jack of 6532, Dalzell Place, Pittsburgh 17, Pennsylvania, U.S.A. has now agreed to our terms for undertaking to develop in all countries in the world except the U.S.A. and Canada the Lockspike invented by him, in respect of which he has made application for a patent in the U.S.A." The American patent was due for issue on October 10th.

The new acquisition was a simple spring spike designed to fix baseplates to timber sleepers. The interesting thing about it was that once it was driven into its pre-bored hole in the sleeper, spring pressure wedged it tightly in the baseplate hole and therefore movement of the baseplate itself, either laterally or vertically, became almost an impossibility.

The development and marketing of the Lockspike was entrusted to a new company which was now set up to deal with track fastenings other than the original Elastic Rail Spike. This was Lockspike Ltd., a wholly owned subsidiary which was incorporated on July 4th 1953. At its first board meeting, on July 28th at the Mayfair Hotel, L. N. Rawes took the chair. Other directors present were Newson, Sanson and H. E. Thompson, and the Company Secretary was L. T. Gardner. Manufacture was to start at Worksop.

Soon an agreement was being negotiated with the firm of Becke-Prinz for the manufacture and sale of Lockspikes in Germany. Other agreements were to follow with people in Sweden and in Italy. There seemed, however, to be little chance of selling the Lockspike in this country since the Elastic Rail Spike was in such widespread use. Until, that is, the Southern Region of British Railways decided to go for an indirect spring rail fastening with steel baseplates. Then it was not long before the Lockspike had completely displaced the traditional screwspike wherever the Southern Region used steel baseplates with wooden sleepers.

The fact that British Railways was now able to get on familiar terms, technically, with the Lockspike was important. It helped lead to its eventual decision to adopt the Lockspike as the standard fastening for securing both cast-iron and steel baseplates to timber sleepers.

By now Lockspike Australia Pty., Ltd. had blossomed on the other side of the world. Production began at Hornsby, New South Wales, in January 1956, and by the early 1970s Australia was to become the biggest producer of Lockspikes anywhere. New South Wales Railways were to standardise on this fastening and consume it at the rate of four million a year. Other major users were to be the Commonwealth Railways, the new coal railways in Queensland and the privately owned iron ore railways. As the need to increase sleeper life became more acute, the demand was to keep on growing.

And at home by 1960 a modification, the Gauge Lockspike, had made its appearance. It had a specially shaped head which allowed it to secure the rail as well as the baseplate, so that no other fastening was necessary.

Meanwhile technical experiments with indirect fastenings had been steadily going on. Back in 1952 there had been an agreement between the ERS Company and one Karl Richard Theodor Wilheim Stamm "in respect of his invention relating to rail fasteners". In 1953 there was Thompson's Starfish Insert Design "concerned with concrete sleepers", which was to be neglected in favour of experimental work with rubber-covered spikes. A considerable amount of money was spent by the company in its attempts to find a satisfactory design, and some of the experiments involved track tests.

Nor was the competition idle. There were a number of other fastenings, most of them designed specifically for use with concrete sleepers, and one in particular—developed on the Western Region of British Railways—found a degree of favour.

The forming of an Elastic Rail Spike at the Claylands Forge Works (*Chapter* 4 *and Chapter* 6).

The forming of a 'Pandrol' Rail Clip, Claylands Forge, Worksop (*Chapter* 6 *and Chapter* 7).

'Pandrol' Rail Clips with new steel sleepers and weld-on shoulder plates at Buxar, India (*Chapter* 3).

The opening of the Nacala Link Line, Malawi Section, a 3 ft 6 in gauge railway using 'Pandrol' Rail Clips (*Chapter* 7).

The driving of Elastic Rail Spikes on the Hedjaz Railway. The mechanical spike driving machine in the background is an Electromatic Tamper (*Chapter* 8).

Elastic Rail Spikes like it hot! A stretch of the rehabilitated Hedjaz line in Jordan (*Chapter* 8).

'Pandrol' track in Western Australia. L. S. Sanson (*right*) with A. B. Holm, Chief Civil Engineer of Western Australia Government Railways (*Chapter* 7).

'Pandrol' links the iron ore mines with the sea. The Hamersley Iron Company's private line in Western Australia (*Chapter* 7).

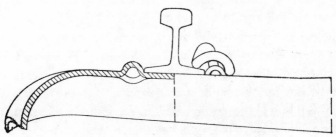

Steel sleeper with "Pandrol" rail fastenings. Half section

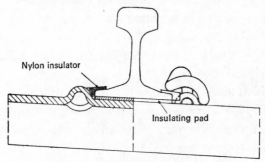

Nylon insulator

Insulating pad

Steel sleeper with "Pandrol" rail fastenings and insulation
for track-circuited lines. Half section

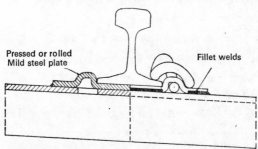

Pressed or rolled
Mild steel plate

Fillet welds

Method of rehabilitating and strengthening old lug or clip
type steel sleepers to carry rails of either similar or
different section. Half section

THE "PANDROL" RAIL FASTENING FOR STEEL SLEEPERS.

PANDROL LT°, 7 ROLLS BUILDINGS, LONDON, EC4. DWG N° 883.

Fig. 5

Yet no single design seemed to have really clicked, either technically or commercially.

During this period one of the places Sanson used to visit regularly on Elastic Rail Spike business was Oslo. Among the people he often saw was Larsen, the Chief Permanent Way Engineer of the Norwegian State Railways, whose lack of enthusiasm for the Spike was doubtless due to the fact that he was himself the co-inventor of an indirect rail fastening known as the Heyback. One day Sanson had a message at his hotel, first thing in the morning, from someone who was downstairs waiting to see him. The early visitor was, it turned out, the other co-inventor of the Heyback fastening who had come along to offer Sanson the opportunity to sell the invention on a worldwide basis.

The invitation was refused. Sanson, although he did not mention it, had already met someone else who had an invention that seemed really quite interesting. This was Per Pande-Rolfsen, a track engineer who was working on Larsen's staff.

Now the normal practice is, at least with railways, that you offer any invention you have come up with during or as a result of your normal work to the company which employs you. If, however, your employers do not take up the offer within six months, you are then free to sell it elsewhere. And so it was that on a later occasion when Sanson was back in Oslo, he was able to say to Larsen, "What do you think of our new fastening?" There was an instant reply. "That's ours!" Whereupon Sanson could retort, "You will find it belongs to a London company".

Immediately recognising the worth of Pande-Rolfsen's design, Sanson had pounced upon it, untested as it was, and acquired the worldwide rights. It had been invented in 1957. By May 6th 1958 an agreement was fixed between Lockspike Ltd. and Moller & Ringstad Export Co., A/S of Sandvika, Oslo, whereby "certain patents and patent applications . . .

concerning the Pandrol fastening" were assigned to the British company. Sanson's new rail fastening clip had been christened in honour of its inventor with two syllables from his name.

Experimental production of the Pandrol Clip was soon under way at Worksop. Here was an indirect fastening substantially different in principle from any other in existence, a simple spring clip which exploited the flexibility of a bar of steel with a cool new virtuosity and promised to solve so many problems with the greatest of ease. You made it from silico-manganese spring steel bar of circular section, appropriately hardened and tempered. To accommodate it, you also made a housing incorporated in a cast-iron or steel baseplate which was to be fixed to the sleeper. When it came to installation on the track, you drove the clip into place, parallel to the rail, with an ordinary 7 lb. plate-layer's hammer. One end of the clip engaged in a slot in the baseplate, while the other held the rail foot with a frictional grip. It was as if the rail were being pinioned by someone's curvaceous yet extremely muscular elbow.

Yet the frictional force between clip and housing was two or three times greater than that between clip and rail. This meant longitudinal movement of the rail—'rail creep'— could not shift the clip from its position in the housing. In other words, the Pandrol Clip could not possibly work loose. Not surprisingly, the selling slogan soon to be adopted for Pandrol was "Fit and Forget".

The toe of the clip, furthermore—the part of it resting on the rail foot—imposed a vertical load which held the rail firmly in position yet at the same time allowed controlled vertical movement under traffic. And these actions of the clip did not depend upon the skill of the man who fitted it. They were predetermined in the design. Another thing was that the clip could be removed just as easily as it could be fitted, which meant rail changing and adjustment would be far less of a problem than before.

Briefly, the Pandrol Clip was a fully resilient indirect fastening which could absorb vibrations as a result of traffic without transmitting them to the sleeper. It was destined to become the most versatile clip in the world, equally at home with timber, steel, cast-iron plate and concrete sleepers.

Development work began in 1959. It was done in close conjunction with British Railways' Research Department at Derby, where J. C. Loach was a highly co-operative tower of strength. The first thing was to determine a shape and size that would be suitable for British Railways track loadings. Then there was the question of a baseplate that would go with timber sleepers. Within three years the first test track had been put in at Peterborough, under the auspices of the Eastern Region's Chief Engineer, A. K. (Sandy) Terris, who had originally trained alongside Sanson. Both this and later tests were so successful that British Railways rapidly cottoned on to the Pandrol idea and started asking for the clip for track renewals. Practical and laboratory tests were carried out by Lockspike Ltd. with intensive determination and enthusiasm. They went on for several years. Most of the drawings were done by 'W.J.'—A. I. Webber Jones, ex-Chief Engineer of the Nigerian Railways, whose knowledge of track was formidable. Baseplates were tried in harness with concrete sleepers.

During the 1830s, when he was Engineer-in-Chief for the London & Birmingham line, the celebrated Robert Stephenson was believed to have walked the track—the entire length of it—"no less than fifteen times, which totalled in the region of 1,700 miles". Perhaps Bill Houghton would not claim to have competed with that extraordinary feat, yet while the Pandrol development work was going on he certainly knocked up more than a mile or two. His copy of the standard British Railways atlas was soon peppered with little yellow dotted lines. These indicated where "W.G.H. has walked". That is to say, walked the track.

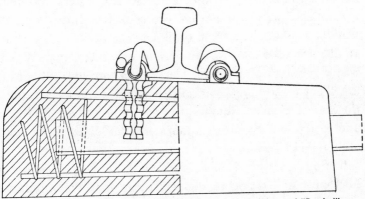

Tied-block concrete sleeper with cast-in malleable-iron shoulders and "Pandrol"
rail fastenings.

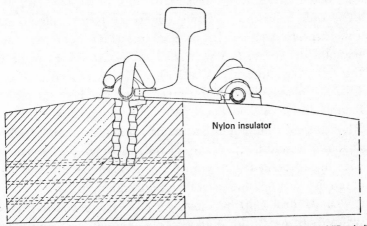

Nylon insulator

Transverse prestressed concrete sleeper with cast-in malleable-iron shoulders and "Pandrol"
rail fastenings. Nylon insulators for track-circuited lines are provided. Half section.

THE "PANDROL" RAIL FASTENING FOR CONCRETE SLEEPERS.

PANDROL LTD, 7 ROLLS BUILDINGS, LONDON, ECA. Dwg Nº 882.

Fig. 6

On one occasion he went down to Totnes in Devon where his host, Ashley Burgess, whom he had not previously met, addressed him thus: "I understand from the D.E. you are to accompany me in the normal course of my duty. Well, I'm walking to Brent . . . if you think you can do it." They set off. It did not take long for Burgess to appreciate that W.G.H. was a genuine railwayman. Sleeper pacing, after all, was an art. That crusty mood vanished, and the two men were soon the best of friends. (Houghton, it should be added, still 'walks' and has probably covered more sections of track than any other man in Britain.)

Sanson became Chairman and Managing Director of Lockspike Ltd. on September 1st 1961, upon the withdrawal of L. N. Rawes. By January 1963 the manufacture of the clip was being arranged in Australia, and Lockspike Australia Pty., Ltd. being given selling rights in New Zealand and Indonesia as well as its own country. By February 1964 manufacture in Austria was lined up. South Africa came in the following June, the Elastic Rail Spike Company (Pty.) Ltd. in Johannesburg being given the right both to manufacture and to sell in South Africa, Southern and Northern Rhodesia, Mozambique, Swaziland, Basutoland and Bechuanaland. And in the February of 1965 there was an agreement with S.A. Rocribel with regard to the manufacture and sale of the clip in Belgium, Holland and Luxembourg.

The Pandrol Clip had found itself being developed more swiftly both on British Railways and abroad than any other rail fastening that had been devised. It was not long, in fact, before the company's patent agent was getting the jitters in case rights to the registered trade mark represented by the word 'Pandrol' might be lost since those seven letters had come to describe a type of fastening and had passed into international usage. Such, within a very short space of time, was Pandrol's fame in railway circles.

Final acceptance by British Railways came in 1965 when the clip was made a standard fastening for wooden sleepers. At the same time it was also adopted as standard for all concrete sleeper track renewals, as from 1966 onwards. Baseplates similar to those used with wooden sleepers had been tried on concrete sleepers, but during 1963 a much simpler and more efficient assembly had been developed which dispensed with baseplates altogether. Shoulders of steel or malleable iron were introduced, being cast into the sleeper during manufacture. It was this adaptation of Pandrol to fit concrete sleepers, devised by Trevor Astley and first tested near Northampton in December 1963, which clinched the clip's future from the point of view of British Railways.

That decision to standardise meant in effect that a million sleepers a year would be incorporating the Pandrol fastening. Six hundred miles of track, in fact, with concrete sleepers and over two hundred with timber. To the tune of seven million Pandrol Clips per annum.

On October 5th 1965 A. Paterson, Chief Civil Engineer of British Railways, wrote to Sanson. "Since the flat-bottomed rail came into general use in Great Britain", he said, "many different types of fastenings have been produced. The 'Pandrol' clip for use on the baseplate on timber sleepers, or on the malleable cast shoulder block in pre-stressed concrete sleepers, is considered to be the most satisfactory fastening yet devised. British Railways will standardise on the 'Pandrol' for both timber and concrete sleeper track as from 1966."

The Annual Report of the British Railways Board for the year ended December 31st 1965 contained this statement: "During the year, 550 miles of track were relaid with continuous welded rail on concrete sleepers, making a total of some 2,350 miles on principal routes. The Pandrol type of track fastening, which has technical and economic advantages, was adopted as standard."

Virtually simultaneous with the switch to Pandrol was British Railways' adoption of the Lockspike as its standard fastening for securing Pandrol baseplates to wooden sleepers. And so it was that on August 25th 1965 the Board of the Elastic Rail Spike Company was able to congratulate Sanson on his success "when he reported that he had obtained for the first time in the history of the company a composite order dated 4th August for the supply of Pandrol Rail Clips, Lockspikes and Elastic Rail Spikes required by British Railways from 1st January 1966". The contract stated that the arrangement was to "continue on an open ended basis, subject to either party having the right to terminate the contract by giving twelve months' notice to the other party".

For two linked companies to find themselves asked to supply British Railways with all three of its standard fastenings, continuously yet without an annual contract, was to say the least an unusual situation, and could be attributed to the reliance placed upon deliveries, to the fair price policy maintained, and to the reputation the companies had built for not misusing their patents. From a commercial viewpoint, for example, Lockspike Ltd. had benefited from its policy of allowing railways to obtain components for the Pandrol Assembly from any source they wished provided the Pandrol Clips themselves were bought either from or by arrangement with the company.

So the Pandrol Clip and the Lockspike became inseparable companions as far as timber sleepers were concerned. And Pandrol on its own became a runaway success. In the United Kingdom the situation was soon to be reached, however, where sales could not be increased. For, in due course, all that could be done with regard to British Railways would be the servicing of clips and assemblies which had already been supplied and the maintenance of adequate stocks to meet future demands as they came. Again, therefore, efforts had to be directed towards export.

Another important development was necessary—the adaptation of the clip for use with steel sleepers, which were so widely favoured in tropical countries. During work on this it happened that specially made steel baseplates were welded on to old steel sleepers which were otherwise unfit for service. The result was that the sleepers became even stronger than new ones of similar design, and that it was shown they could be used with a modern resilient fastening.

Fortuitously, the Nigerian Railways Corporation found itself faced with the task of replacing several hundreds of thousands of steel sleepers, which had apparently just about reached the end of their useful life. Many of them were forty years old. At the beginning of 1960, 6,000 sleepers were reconditioned on an experimental basis, Pandrol pressed steel plates being welded to them. An initial test was carried out on three miles of old track. The Chief Engineer, who at that time happened to be Webber Jones, was delighted. A large scale programme was soon in hand. Other methods of rehabilitating ageing steel sleepers had been investigated for comparison, yet the Pandrol way had proved far and away the most economical. And the simplest. African welders were trained for the job in roughly four weeks. By 1969 more than 400,000 steel sleepers had been reconditioned in this manner by the Nigerian Railways Corporation. Similar work was to be done elsewhere in Africa, and also in India and Australia.

Before long the Pandrol Clip had become the standard rail fastening for the Norwegian State Railway (with concrete sleepers), the Stockholm Underground Railway (wooden sleepers), and both the Nigerian Railways and the Sierra Leone Development Co. Railway (steel sleepers).

It was adopted as a standard fastening by South African Railways in 1967, and rapidly found itself meeting 75% of

G

South Africa's requirements for concrete sleepers. Pandrol
it was, indeed, which turned the tide against which the ERS
Company (Pty.) Ltd. had struggled when it had just the
Elastic Rail Spike to offer. A separate subsidiary company was
eventually formed to deal with the marketing and servicing
side of it, under the name of Pandrol (Pty.) Ltd., at the start
of 1973. First General Manager was Graham King, who had
earlier devised the insulator used with the Pandrol Clip in
South Africa and who remained responsible for all technical
research and development in connection with the fastening.
By this time upwards of a million concrete sleepers a year were
being fitted with Pandrol.

The manufacture of Pandrol Clips was, and still is, carried
out by the original ERS Company (Pty.) Ltd. at its Isando
Works, where L. van Aardt was to become Works Manager.
Pandrol's success in South Africa led to its use in Rhodesia
where sub-contractors started manufacture both of the clip
and of associated components. It also pushed its way into
Mozambique where, in Lourenco Marques, a company was
recently established under the name of Pandrol Ltda., Mocam-
bique to undertake manufacture under sub-licence. Pandrol
has been adopted as the standard fastening for concrete
sleepers in this territory, where the C.F.M. has ordered
300,000 sleepers to be fitted with it. The clip was used on the
Malawi section of the Nacala Link Line, a 3 ft 6 in. gauge
railway, which was officially opened by President Banda.
Both Ernest Gearing, Managing Director of the South African
group of companies, and Bill Houghton, 'ambassador-at-
large', became good friends with Malawi's Minister of Transport, John Msonthi, as this project progressed.

A million clips a year started being taken in 1972 by the
East African Railways Corporation for its famous line from
the coast to Uganda. A trial track was laid in Madagascar.

THE CHANGE OVER FROM BROAD TO NARROW GAUGE

"The change over from broad to narrow gauge", as seen by W. Heath Robinson. Gauge-chauging can be done somewhat more easily nowadays with the aid of Peter Davies' gauge-changing device. In East Africa, as a result, Pandrol steel sleepers are convertible from metre to 3ft 6in gauge.

By courtesy of Mrs Josephine Heath Robinson

And back in 1969 Pandrol was supplied to the Société des Chemins de Fer Vicinaux du Congo.

February 1971 saw a new plant being built at Seven Hills, the Australian company's headquarters, solely for the manufacture of Pandrol. It was designed to produce 3.5 to four million clips a year from a single work shift, and with multiple shifts was to be capable of an output as high as twelve million clips per annum. Pandrol was first used in large quantities in Australia, with steel sleepers, by the Commonwealth Railways south of Darwin in the Northern Territory. The line to Alice Springs was four hundred miles long and went through a very hot and arid area. Nobody would work there. So Pandrol Clips solved the desert maintenance problem beautifully. No maintenance became necessary.

Then there were the privately owned railways serving the iron ore mines in the north-west of Western Australia. Each of them was faced with the problem of building a railway from the iron ore mountains to the sea a hundred miles away. The Managing Director of the Hamersley Iron Company, a member company of Conzinc Rio Tinto of Australia Ltd., decided that Pandrol was the answer. After all, it needed no maintenance. So it was used with timber sleepers on a fifty-mile stretch of line designed to take 32-ton axle loads. At first dogspikes had been tried, with heavy rails and heavy sleepers, but within three years everything had started falling to pieces.

First railway in Australia to be entirely constructed with concrete sleepers and Pandrol was the line from Port Augusta to Whyalla, opened late in 1972. The clip was by now also in use in New Zealand, while the upgrading of track in Indonesia was being carried out with Pandrol Clips and Lockspikes supplied from Australia, under the provisions of the Colombo Plan. The Australian Government had said that it thought Pandrol was necessary, and that it would arrange to supply the fastenings.

Manufacture of Pandrol in India, which had been mooted at the request of the Indian Government in early 1967, was eventually started under licence by Guest Keen Williams Ltd., a subsidiary of GKN, at Bangalore. Good relations were established with the Indian Railway Board, and the Pandrol Assembly became a standard fitting for concrete, steel and timber sleepers.

Elsewhere, manufacture was begun on a smaller scale in Austria, Italy and Finland. Production of Pandrol Clips in Austria was entrusted to the long established works of Bohler Bros., but the Elastic Rail Spike sales agency remained with the redoubtable blonde Mrs. Bertha Haag. In Finland Oy Fiskars of Helsinki received a sole although non-exclusive licence for Pandrol. Licensees in Italy were Simmel Industrie Meccaniche S.p.A. of Castelfranco Veneto, who had been in on the manufacture of the Elastic Rail Spike, and Ing. G. & A. Punzi.

The sales drive went on everywhere. In Rumania, a two-kilometre test track was laid in 1969 at Filiasi, and the clip had penetrated the iron curtain. In West Germany, a trial track of 1600 concrete sleepers incorporating Pandrol was put down in the spring of 1973. There were orders from Iraq, and trial lengths were required in Malaysia and Siam.

Over in Brazil, Molas Scripelliti S.A. of São Paulo, which had been producing Elastic Rail Spikes under licence for some years, was now preparing for the production of Lockspikes and Pandrol Clips also. During 1971 control of that company was acquired by the German Hoesch Group, but marketing of the rail fastenings remained firmly in the hands of Oswaldo Rodrigues—the original key man of Parson & Crosland, the selling agents in this territory since the earliest days of ERS. An agreement between Pandrol Ltd. and Hoesch Scripelliti S.A. Industria de Molas came into effect on June 18th 1971.

Pandrol Limited? Yes, for at an Extraordinary General Meeting of Lockspike Ltd. held on June 16th 1970 it was resolved that the company should change its name. From July 1st onwards it was to concern itself solely with the 'Pandrol' Rail Fastening system, while all its business connected with the Lockspike system was to be transferred to a newly acquired fellow subsidiary company within the Group, itself currently known as Pandrol Limited but from now on to be called Lockspike Limited. In other words, two Group companies were swapping names. The new Lockspike Ltd., under its previous name, had been in fact a company without a job. There had been other metamorphoses in its life. Before being incorporated as Pandrol Ltd. in October 1968, it had been known as the British South Africa Company Citrus Products Limited. Its origins as a company reached back to a period before the ERS Group of Companies became a part of the Charter Group.

When Sanson retired as Chairman and Managing Director of Lockspike Ltd., as it then was, at the end of 1969, he was presented as a token of esteem with a Pandrol Clip, the 250 millionth rail fastening to have come off the production line. His place in the chair was taken by George Flint and as M.D. by Trevor Astley. Flint himself retired three months later, and as from April 1st Astley was Chairman.

By the end of 1971 over 67 million 'Pandrol' Rail Clips had been produced. And selling abroad was continuing unabated. In February 1973 Len Gardner supervised the setting up of a subsidiary in Spain, Pandrol Iberica S.A., deploying for the umpteenth time his valuable knowledge and experience of the vagaries of company law overseas. The prospects of tapping the enormous American market showed signs of improvement, despite almost equally enormous obstacles such as the fact that U.S. railways engineers, almost to a man, were wary of a departure from their traditional 'cut spike and anchor' track construction. An agreement was reached as far back as 1966 with Evans Products Company of Plymouth,

Michigan, relating to the manufacture and sale of manufacture and sale of 'Pandrol' Rail Clips. In 1970, following Evans' decision to concentrate their efforts in the rolling stock market, the Pandrol agency was transferred, by mutual agreement, to Unit Rail Anchor Company Inc. of Pittsburgh. Various railroad companies have now put in installations on both timber and concrete crossties. In Canada, after obtaining experience from several small installations, the Canadian National Railway has installed a major test on concrete crossties; the successful performance of this length is likely to affect track developments significantly in North America as a whole.

Much of the burden of the original missionary work on behalf of Pandrol in North America was borne by Trevor Astley. When he became Managing Director in 1970, the tough task he had undertaken was carried on by Trevor Brown, who was now Pandrol Ltd.'s Technical Director. T. P. Brown's involvement with North American railways was soon to become so deep that he found himself being invited to sit on the American Concrete Institute's Committee 545 on Concrete Railroad Ties—in order to offer the benefits of his experience of the rail fastenings which form such a vital part of successful concrete tie design. Like Astley, he was also to join the ranks of the American Railway Engineering Association.

Trevor 'B''s experiences include one or two which illustrate some of the hazards of travelling to the extent that the company's export effort requires. He was lucky to escape with bruises when the *Broadway Limited* on which he was travelling between Baltimore and Chicago was in a disastrous derailment at 3 a.m. in a March blizzard. He had been in another derailment a little while earlier on his way from London to Worksop in 1971.

Plagiarism of the Pandrol principle had been attempted. Applications for patents were put in hand "in connection with a rail clip whose design originated in Japan" during 1966 and

1967. The astute Sanson, on the ball as ever, had scotched the opposition by buying it up.

Pandrol's progress in the United Kingdom has not been limited to the networks of British Rail. The London Transport Executive became another customer, as did the Northern Ireland Railway Co. Ltd. which took delivery of components for 33,000 concrete sleepers during 1971, the first year of a five-year programme. Industrial users of the clip in Britain include the National Coal Board and the British Steel Corporation.

Continental countries which have gone either firmly or partially on to 'the Pandrol standard' are Austria (Austrian Federal Railways are using a variety of assemblies), Belgium (Belgian National Railways experimenting with Pandrol plus concrete sleepers, after extensive use with wooden sleepers for relaying track in tunnels), Finland (standard with concrete sleepers, and being used in the Helsinki Metro), Italy (227,000 clips installed with concrete sleepers by Italian State Railways, after first experience in 1961 with wooden sleepers), Norway (standard with concrete since 1966 on Norwegian State Railways, and adopted by Oslo Underground Railway for wood and concrete), and Sweden (used by State Railways with concrete in main line track, standard on Stockholm Underground since 1960, and used by Gothenburg Tramways). Trial installations have extended the arena to Ireland, West Germany and Rumania.

In and around Africa, Pandrol has found its way to the East African Community countries (where the introduction of Pandrol steel sleepers, easily convertible from metre to 3ft 6in gauge, has been important), Malagasy (for rehabilitating steel sleepers), Malawi, Mozambique, Nigeria (where the clip is standard), Sierra Leone (50-mile iron ore railway completely relaid with Pandrol and steel sleepers, 1962–63), South Africa, and Zaire (over a million clips ordered to go with steel sleepers). Trials have been undertaken in Zambia and the Sudan.

After seven years of trials in India, a starting order for a million clips came in, manufacture being carried out locally by the licensee, Guest Keen Williams. Taiwan and Malaysia have taken test lengths, as Indonesia did in 1971 (in Java) before it was decided to put down 150 kilometres of track there with Pandrol securing both timber and steel sleepers. After taking 55,000 Pandrol concrete sleepers from the Australians, New Zealand ordered up clips for use with timber sleepers on fifty miles of track.

Among the users in Australia are Commonwealth Railways (with 400,000 steel sleepers plus Pandrol on the North Australia Railway), New South Wales Government Railways, Western Australian Government Railways, the Comaleo company (for the new bauxite railway in northern Queensland), and the Hamersley Iron Company. Two lines being upgraded with Pandrol are one between Mount Tom Price and Paraburdoo, and another from Dampier to Tom Price, on timber sleepers. Here the traffic consists of mile-long trains each carrying 16,000 tons of iron ore.

'Pandrolisation' in the western hemisphere has so far reached Canada (initial trials being followed up with a severe test of 10,000 concrete sleepers), Costa Rica (first-time 10,000 concrete sleeper installation), Guyana (industrial user undertaking test), Jamaica (regular use with concrete by Jamaica Railway Corporation, plus trial by mining company), Mexico (preliminary trial with concrete by National Railways, and local manufacture in the offing), and the United States.

The rapid and sustained spread of Pandrol overseas has undoubtedly encouraged exports by other British companies with which the ERS group has no connection and from whose efforts it does not benefit financially. One Australian order for Pandrol, for example, resulted in an opportunity being opened up for the export of 150,000 steel sleepers from the United Kingdom. The Group's export mania is contagious.

A Desert Saga

It was on May 16th 1962 that Stewart Sanson raised at a board meeting a subject which was to acquire, during the course of the next eight years or so, something of the quality of a recurring nightmare, although it was also to represent a trading achievement of considerable size. The company had, said the Managing Director, been invited by a Japanese firm called Marubeni-Ida Co. Ltd. to submit a tender on a credit basis in connection with the rebuilding of the Hedjaz Railway.

Talk had been going on for some forty years about rehabilitating this pilgrims' line from Damascus to Medina, which had been commissioned in 1901 by Abdul-Hamid II, Sultan of Turkey, in order to provide easier access to the holy city of Mecca, and completed in 1908, only to be wrecked by T. E. Lawrence in 1917. Now at last it seemed matters were coming to a head. The governments of Syria, Jordan and Saudi Arabia had agreed to co-operate on the project and were setting up a committee—the Hedjaz Railway Committee—to supervise it.

Contributions towards the cost were expected to come from devout Moslems everywhere, just as they had when the line was originally constructed. They had then subscribed over £1 million. The Sultan himself had put £50,000 into the kitty, to which was added the 10% of one month's wages he had ordered to be stopped from each and every soldier and official in the Ottoman Empire. The men who built the railway were a cosmopolitan crowd—Greeks, Italians, Germans, Turks, Montenegrins, Syrians—but the engineers were German, the Engineer-in-Chief being the legendary Meissner Pasha. The contract had been a prize won through the Kaiser's assiduous wooing of Turkey at that time. Another prize had been the decision to go ahead with the Berlin-Baghdad Railway, a bright idea launched by the Deutsche Bank, which however even by 1914 had progressed very little.

Curiously, nevertheless, it had been Queen Victoria who had in a sense sparked off the idea of the Hedjaz Railway when she wrote to Abdul-Hamid complaining about the "great sufferings" her Moslem subjects had to put up with when they undertook the pilgrimage. Not that the Sultan's motives were solely religious, let alone diplomatic. He was keen to provide rail access to Arabia for his troops as well as for the devotees of the Prophet.

The line was meant to reach Mecca itself from Damascus a thousand miles away, but it never did. "The Hejaz tribes", in the words of James Morris, "angrily objected to the completion of the railway, which would rob them of income both as camel-owners and as potential bandits". Nor would Hussein, the Grand Sharif of Mecca, collaborate, since he was now at odds with the Turkish central government.

All the same, the arrival of the railway at Medina meant that the journey time for pilgrims shrank to three days from the traditional six weeks by caravan, tortoise-slow though the trains were. Until, that is, the war changed things. "There followed a terrific roar, and the line vanished from sight behind a spouting column of black dust and smoke a hundred feet high and wide," recorded Lawrence in his account of the exploits of September 1917. "Out of the darkness came shattering crashes and long, loud metallic clangings of ripped steel, with many lumps of iron and plate; while one entire wheel of a locomotive whirled up suddenly black out of the cloud against the sky, and sailed musically over our heads to fall slowly and heavily into the desert behind. Except for the flight of these, there succeeded a deathly silence, with no cry of men or rifle-shot, as the now grey mist of the explosion drifted from the line towards us, and over our ridge until it was lost in the hills."

Despite the havoc he and his dynamite wrought, Lawrence hoped, as he told General Allenby, "to leave the line just working, but only just, to Medina". It was in fact trains he attacked rather than the line itself. And the Hedjaz Railway was still working after a fashion long after the war had ended. In 1921 the Amir Abdullah, later to become Jordan's first king, commandeered a train, set off from Medina and suc-ceeded in reaching Ma'an, although "the engine had no fuel", and "every few miles they had to stop and chop down a few telegraph poles to sustain the furnace. Sometimes they came to a break in the line, a relic of the war, and a breakdown party would leap from the carriages to repair it."

Abdullah's brother, the Amir Ali, somehow managed to take several trains up from Medina to Amman three years later in 1924, although "not without local difficulties", as H. St. John Philby noted. But during World War II the situation changed entirely, for the line between Ma'an and Mudaw-wara some sixty miles to the south was taken up and relaid in the direction of Aqaba.

Arab vandals had also extracted their toll, stripping "the woodwork of all station buildings for their domestic purposes". Luckily the sleepers were steel ones, "to defeat the machina-tions of the Badawin (Bedouin), who would have found timber sleepers all too useful for their camp-fires". The words, once more, of the explorer Philby who in 1957 complained: "It may be that thirty years of jejune talk about the restoration of the Hijaz Railway to life will shortly make way for actual work on the repair and re-equipment of the line, though it is still too soon to be really optimistic, as the present phase of the project has already been under discussion for nearly three years."

By 1962, when the discussion had finally become pretty warm, the project was being defined as "the Rehabilitation of the Hedjaz Railway from Ma'an, in the Hashemite Kingdom of Jordan, to Medina, in the Kingdom of Saudi Arabia". The line between Damascus and Ma'an was, on the whole, still intact, and 75% of the bridges were in good fettle. The section of the railway to be rebuilt covered a distance of 566 miles, and the estimated total cost was soon to be quoted as £7,250,000.

Following the Elastic Rail Spike Company's receipt of its invitation to tender, it decided to send somebody out to the Middle East to take stock of the situation. Soon Lt. Col. Peter Davies was in Damascus, where he quickly realised that intensive competition would have to be overcome if the company's product was to win and be chosen as the standard rail fastening for the project.

The opposition, not surprisingly, came from Germany. The original railway had been built, after all, by German engineers, so it was quite reasonable for their successors to regard the Hedjaz line as being within their legitimate sphere of influence. The manufacturers of a German rail fastening somewhat similar to the Elastic Rail Spike had their eyes on the contract that the ERS Company also sought. Furthermore, there were German consulting engineers on the spot already. They were supervising the construction of Damascus Airport.

A season of healthy rivalry set in. A spell of particularly bad weather, from the point of view of London, blew in over the question of the specification for the rail spikes to be used. It seemed at one moment that the steel specification laid down by the German consulting engineers would give the company's competitors the edge and that their fastening would be chosen. But by the time the clouds had cleared, the brilliant light of the Middle Eastern sun was shining upon the authentic Elastic Rail Spike.

In the meantime there had been a fresh development.

The contract for repairing the Ma'an–Medina line had initially been awarded, during 1962, to the Ibn Ladin Company of Saudi Arabia and to Marubeni-Ida, the Japanese firm which had invited the ERS Company to tender for spikes. But by September 1963 this contract had been cancelled, the job having already been put out to international tender.

It was reported, on March 27th 1963, "that a British Consortium is being formed by Thomas Summerson & Sons Ltd. by means of a company limited by guarantee and this Company has agreed to become a member of the Consortium". Summerson's was a firm from Durham which laid claim to having been the world's first railway track engineers. Its founder had helped to build the Stockton and Darlington Railway of 1823–25.

The consortium, initially known as the Summerson Overseas Railway Development Consortium, consisted of eight separate companies. Thomas Summerson's themselves were to be the Managing Agents, with overall responsibility for the supply of all materials, the laying of the track, the rebuilding of stations, the installation of water supplies and the maintenance of communications. Their particular role within the consortium was to be to supervise the track laying, to manufacture and install the turnouts and crossings, and to look after communications. The consulting engineers were Livesey & Henderson Associates Ltd. The rails were to come from United Steel Companies Ltd., the fishbolts, nuts and washers from GKN (Bolts & Nuts) Ltd., and the sleepers—to be made of jarrah, an Australian hardwood—from Millars Timber & Trading Co. Ltd. and from May & Hassel (Hardwoods) Ltd. Henville Ltd. were to supply the water pumps, culverts and electrical equipment, and the Elastic Rail Spike Co. Ltd. the rail spikes.

The idea was to start work at both ends of the railway at the same time—at Ma'an and Medina—and to complete the job in two years, installing track at the rate of 1½ kilometres a day. The preliminary tender was placed on March 5th 1963, and outline proposals were submitted on March 25th. These proposals were discussed with the Hedjaz Railway Committee in Damascus on April 16th, and on April 27th a further discussion was held between George Rennie of Summerson's and Ahmed Fawzi, later to become Chairman of the Committee. Complete technical and financial proposals were presented in May. Among the items of track material specified were 'elastic rail spikes type Rueping T3 and type Rueping T4', the quantities quoted being 2½ million of the former and 1,050,000 of the latter.

At a board meeting of the ERS Company on September 25th it was decided that the company would now agree to go ahead with joining the consortium company only 'if and when' the agreements were satisfactory. There was no intention of accepting "responsibility for onerous terms accepted by Summerson Overseas Railway Development Co. Ltd. or for other material suppliers or for the constructing company's defaults".

In fact the consortium never quite succeeded in getting off the ground. For the contract had gone to a rival consortium formed by Alderton Construction Westminister Ltd. and Martin Cowley Ltd., who had set up a company called Hedjaz Construction Co. Ltd. to whom the ERS Company had tendered for the supply of spikes. So the main contractors were British, but the consulting engineers were German—Dipl. Ing. K. Becker G.m.b.H. of Munich.

Was the Elastic Rail Spike in fact going to be chosen? The situation was still clouded with uncertainty. On July 30th 1964 Peter Davies gave vent to his feelings of frustration in a letter to Waddah Djabri, the company's agent on the spot. "It does seem that the Committee are taking a very long time to come to a decision", he wrote, "and when you say that Elastic Rail Spikes are on the Agenda, we assume you mean that the point at issue is whether or not the Spikes are to be to our finish, which is the correct one . . ." But the deliberations of the Hedjaz Railway Committee were not to be hurried. During that same year its Chairman, Fouad El-Halaby, died. The pace of negotiation faltered, then began once more to regain its mulishly gentle momentum.

By the beginning of 1967 everything had suddenly moved into a gallop. Thomas Summerson's were still officially in charge of the track laying, but the main contractors were now Martin Cowley Railway Construction Co. Ltd. operating alone. And the previous November a letter had gone to Martin Cowley from Engineer Samih Fakhoury, Director General of the Hedjaz Railway Recommissioning Authority, stating that the original specifications for railway fastenings were being maintained "in respect of the line between Tebuk and Medina".

In response to a firm order from Martin Cowley for 2,200,000 Elastic Rail Spikes, the first consignment of 150,000 T3 and T4 types had already been sent on its way before the New Year had dawned. Stocks of rail and of jarrah sleepers had beaten the spikes to it and were now on the site where tracking laying was due to start.

Understandably, however, the company was anxious about what would happen to the spikes when they arrived. Correct installation was vital if they were to give satisfactory service. Martin Cowley had been offered the services of an engineer who could show their local platelayers the right way to do it. He was all set to wing off to Amman. But so far the offer had not been accepted.

Trevor Astley took up the matter with Sir Maurice Adams of Summerson's, who explained that his own firm's Chief Engineer, Major Norris, was out in Amman and that it would be his responsibility to see that the spikes were properly driven. Summerson's were not undertaking the track laying operations, but they were supervising them. If the ERS Company wanted to send someone out to meet Norris on the site, that would be fine, but arrangements for this had better be made with Martin Cowley, the main contractor.

Notwithstanding such tepid encouragement, and despite Martin Cowley's reaction of a fortnight or so later ("Not quite ready for him"), Bill Houghton was shortly on his way east, determined to see to it that the spikes were correctly installed from the start.

Nor was the company's concern limited to that which it felt for its own product. Moves had been made to arrange the secondment of an engineer with the necessary railway knowledge from British Railways, so that he could fill the gap which clearly appeared to exist among the ranks of those engaged upon the Hedjaz project. As Stewart Sanson pointed out, "British interests were of great importance in that part of the world and the British Embassy in Damascus had previously expressed concern at the damage to British interests that would be done if the job was not carried out properly". And so, by mid-February, a senior British Railways man was on the scene in Jordan, in an advisory capacity.

On January 18th 1967 the *Daily Telegraph* reported that four British steel companies were to supply equipment worth well over £1 million for rebuilding the southern section of the Hedjaz Railway. The contract called for 28,000 tons of rails and other equipment. Main contractors were Colvilles, the Scottish steel group, the other firms being Dorman Long, Workington Iron & Steel (part of the United Steel Group), and South Durham Steel & Iron. Six days later there appeared an advertisement in the same newspaper. A track engineer was required by a British/Middle East company of engineering contractors. It was Summerson's.

The following morning Rex Saggers, Managing Director of Martin Cowley, the main contractors, was interviewed on the BBC's *Today* programme. Speeds of up to 40 m.p.h. would be

H

possible on the new railway, he said. Rail fastenings received
no mention, although the jarrah sleepers from Australia did.

It was February by the time the Elastic Rail Spike gained its
small share of publicity. "A Worksop firm", announced the
Sheffield Star, "has been working flat out to complete on schedule
a Middle East order for 2,250,000 rail fastening spikes. Today
the *Star* learned that the company are negotiating a new contract which could mean another huge order." Stewart Sanson
was reported as saying: "This is one of the most important
export orders this company has ever had". He had also added
that "because of delay caused by the political climate and
upheavals out there it has taken five and a half years to get
this order". The spikes, said the paper, were being shipped to
Syria and Jordan in three 300-ton loads. The total quantity
amounted to 917 tons.

Shipments were made aboard vessels chartered by Colvilles,
which had originally been intended to unload at Beirut.
They were however re-routed to Aqaba, the Jordanian port
at the head of the hundred-mile-long Gulf of Aqaba—the
easternmost of those two snail's horns of water at the head of
the Red Sea.

Sanson had referred to political upheavals. There had
indeed been one or two. Back in the early 'sixties, following the
disintegration of his United Arab Republic, Nasser had become
involved in a conflict with Saudi Arabia over the Yemen, and
was also at odds with the secessionist Syrians. In 1963 there
was a coup in Syria, to be outmatched by another in February
1966. The commandos of the Palestine Liberation Organisation
were officially placed under Syrian command, and now there
was a spate of raids and counter-raids across the Israeli frontier.
The go-ahead for the Hedjaz Railway project could not have
come at a less auspicious time.

As the materials for the track laying were arriving at Aqaba,
the political temperature was rising fast to crisis heat. In May

1967 United Nations troops in the Sinai Peninsula were being thrown out of their positions by Nasser's forces. Ahmed Shukairy, head of the P.L.O., exhorted the people of Jordan to get rid of their king. And on May 23rd, while Jordan was expelling the Syrian Ambassador from Amman and pulling its own Charge d'Affaires out of Damascus, and while King Feisal of Saudi Arabia was on a state visit to Britain, Nasser suddenly blockaded the entrance to the Gulf of Aqaba—the Straits of Tiran. No ships bound for the Israeli port of Eilat were to be let through, although vessels heading for Aqaba were unaffected. But mines, said Egypt, had been laid, and all ships would be searched.

Now Jordan's troops took up their battle positions. The Egyptian General Riad took over command and units from several Arab states began arriving in Amman and elsewhere. A couple of Saudi Arabian brigades were poised at Tebuk, on the route of the Hedjaz Railway, ready to move north. The inevitable war began on Monday June 5th.

In what has been described as "one of the most rapid and dramatic campaigns in modern history", Israel inflicted a crushing defeat upon the forces of Egypt, Syria, Jordan and their allies. Although described as the Six-Day War, effectively it was lost and won within eighty hours. The air forces of the three Arab countries were just about totally destroyed on the first day. Egypt lost an army of almost 100,000 men in Sinai, along with between six and eight hundred tanks. By June 10th all was over. The U.N. Security Council's cease-fire calls were obeyed.

Predictably, Aqaba had come in for a dose of bombing. No freight destined for the Hedjaz Railway had in fact been hit. In any case consignments of Elastic Rail Spikes were being despatched on an f.o.b. (free on board) basis. Once aboard the ship, they automatically became the property of the customer.

Meanwhile, back at home, Thomas Summerson's had been

running into financial difficulties. Their involvement in the Hedjaz project had proved disastrous, and by July 18th a meeting of their creditors was being held. The company had gone into liquidation.

But work on the railway went on. Not as rapidly as Martin Cowley had anticipated, for they had expected to lay three miles of track a day. In other words, one rail length of track every two minutes, which was absurdly optimistic, to say the least. In any case the adzing and boring machine, which inclined the rail seat at the correct slope and bored the holes in the sleepers for the rail spikes, could manage only about eight hundred sleepers a day.

Since the sleepers were of hardwood, no baseplates were being used. With regard to these hardwood sleepers, one senior engineer from British Railways to whom Peter Davies spoke believed that local workmen would not be able to drive T type Spikes into them. Davies had replied that the company had "ample proof that this was possible—from West Africa."

Nevertheless in due course mechanical spike driving machines supplied by Tamper Incorporated of South Carolina were brought in to speed up the work. But by September 1969 these Electromatic Tampers were all out of action, and driving was again being done by hand. It was not until the following summer that the problem was sorted out, the hardwood sleepers from then on being pre-bored at the larger diameter size originally recommended by Bill Houghton, and the difficulty of driving the spikes vertically being overcome through the use of sleeper nippers (which pulled up the sleeper to the rail foot while the spike was being driven).

Of difficulties there had never been any lack. Earlier on, for example, the German consulting engineers had requested that oil should be burnt into the spikes at 400°C. to prevent corrosion. What had not been realised was that oil evaporated at that temperature.

And there was one particular problem which very nearly caused an international incident of the company's very own. On September 19th 1969 a cable arrived in London, addressed to Houghton. "Urgent one day visit Amman required from you or high representative for very important matter," it read. "Kindly cable, regards, Hijazco, Malek." The sender was now Martin Cowley's Manager in Amman, Rex Saggers having been obliged to depart owing to the mercurial political situation.

By September 24th Houghton was on his way to Amman. On arrival next day he ricochetted round to Martin Cowley's offices. Bumping into Abu Masloud, the Line Chief Engineer on the Hedjaz project, he heard about a couple of things which had gone wrong. One was the fact that the nippers had still not been fitted to the spike drivers, and that hole squaring had not started. Another was that the joint gaps on long rails had not been wide enough, since temperatures had soared to 60°C. in the desert that August. Only sixty-five kilometres of track had so far been laid, and that was far behind schedule.

A few moments later Martin Cowley's Chief Engineer, I. Husseini, turned up and said merely that he had heard of "some label offence". It was not till the following morning that Houghton saw Fouad Malek, the man who had summoned him. When the two were alone in his office, Malek locked the door on the inside, and then moved across to a cupboard. Unlocking it, he took out a cardboard box and from this pulled out a bag. Clearly it was the inner part of one of the double bags normally used for holding Elastic Rail Spikes.

Adroitly turning the bag inside out, Malek now held it up. Attached to a corner was a small pressed tag, round and the colour of brass. On one side it bore the numerals '73' and letters 'FM'. On the other, there was a six-pointed star—the Israeli star of David.

After a pause "while I gathered some composure", as Bill Houghton reported, "I detected a familar West African smell of palm kernels". And he remembered that there were Nigerian coins with holes which had the six-pointed star on them. Women used to wear them strung around their waists.

How was it that the company had an Israeli tag on its products, asked Malek, and did it have any dealings with Israel? Houghton replied that the company obtained all its inner bags secondhand, and that that particular bag clearly must have come in the first place from Nigeria.

The offensive piece of jute had apparently been found by a labourer on the railway line who, on spotting the star of David, had taken it straight to Arab Security in Ma'an without reference to his superiors. Security were soon on to Martin Cowley, and half a dozen more labels had been found. It also looked as though labels had been cut off some bags.

Fortunately, said Malek, he had friends in Security at Ma'an, and with any luck he could contain the matter there. If once it were to leak out to Amman, the entire Arab world would know. To ensure that this did not happen, the company would have to supply Security with a full explanation of how such a tag had come to be fixed to its products—in view of the terms of the letter of credit requiring that it had no dealings with Israel. Furthermore, the company would have to state to what extent it had ever had dealings with Israel, and the statements would have to be legalised both by the British Board of Trade and by the Jordanian Embassy in London.

These explanations would need to be provided pretty fast, added Malek, if the company was to avoid being blacklisted throughout the Arab world and by countries sympathetic to the Arab cause.

He also referred in passing to the Hedjaz project itself, saying that at a recent three-nation ministerial meeting Saudi Arabia had refused to contribute any more money for the moment. Jordan and Syria, both much poorer countries, had agreed to put up their shares.

At Malek's request Houghton now went over to Ma'an to attend a meeting with members of the Hedjaz Railway Recommissioning Authority's Technical Bureau and others. Before leaving the Intercontinental Hotel in Amman he hid the controversial sack in his laundry bag, thinking that would seem an innocent place. And it was just as well he had concealed it, for there turned out to be seven road blocks on the way to Ma'an, and one of them was manned by Iraqis, who were by repute tougher customers than the Jordanians.

Then, losing no time, he was on his way back to London, with that trouble-making star of David just about burning a hole in his pocket. Evidence was swiftly mustered to back up his case for the defence. From Quilliam Ltd. in Wednesbury came a letter confirming that the inner bags has been made from sacks which had previously contained palm kernels imported by a Hull firm from West Africa. Enclosed with it was a letter to Quilliam's from Chambers & Fargus Ltd., seed crushers and edible oil refiners in Hull, which stated: ". . . all the empty Palm Kernel Twill Bags we have sold to you have been imported by us containing Nigerian and/or Sierra Leone Palm Kernels and at no time have we received this type of bag from any other source".

The tag had in fact been used by the Agriculture Department of the Nigerian Government as an inspection sign.

And so the suspicions of Arab Security were finally allayed. Other obstacles presented themselves, however, in this seemingly endless Hedjaz steeplechase. When Peter Davies visited Beirut in the November of 1969, no decision had yet been taken about the balance of materials needed to complete the project. The following May Houghton was told by D. A. Kitching, of Millars Timber & Trading who had supplied the jarrah sleepers, that "a critical meeting" was in the offing at which it was to be decided whether or not the whole project should be abandoned. Saudi Arabia had categorically dug in its heels as far as putting in any more money went. In fact, the Saudis did not really want to see the line run beyond Tebuk.

The company's agent, Waddah Djabri, did not think the rehabilitation of the railway would stop in the middle of the desert at Tebuk. The Saudis were refusing to come up with more cash, he felt, because of current political differences with Syria. But eventually they would have to provide it and see the project through, if they were not to lose face on religious grounds.

Yet by April 1971 everything had truly ground to a halt. The Hedjaz Railway, as reconstituted, now petered out some thirty or forty kilometres inside Saudi Arabia.

Roughly three and a quarter million Elastic Rail Spikes and 800,000 jarrah sleepers had, all told, been ordered. Some of course were used. But many, many more were left there in the desert, and there at the time of writing they remain, half buried in their sandy cemetery. Maybe, who knows, they will be used some day.

20. 'Pandrol' Assembly incorporating cast-iron baseplate, Nigerian Railways Corporation.

21. Concrete bearer turnout, incorporating 'Pandrol', British Rail London Midland Region, Radcliffe-on-Trent. *By courtesy of British Rail.*

22. Track of the future? 'Pandrol' in use with non-ballasted track, British Rail. *By courtesy of British Rail.*

23. British Rail's 125 m.p.h. High Speed Train running on 'Pandrol' track. *By courtesy of British Rail.*

Diversification brings a Two-way Stretch

Dr. Angus Smith's Preservative Solution. It sounds a bit like *Alice in Wonderland*, although it is doubtful that this liquid was ever dispensed in a bottle with a paper label round its neck saying "Drink me". What it did was provide a coating of bitumen, for which the original Elastic Rail Spike had a considerable thirst. The spikes were dipped in it—dipped black —when they were first taken by the L.M.S. and the L.N.E.R. for test purposes. It was the same in the case of the S.R. and the G.W.R. later on.

On the G.W.R. the spike's predecessor—on bull-headed track—had been the throughbolt. But on the L.M.S., L.N.E.R. and S.R. it had been the screwspike, and this had normally been galvanized. So, not unnaturally, when the railways realised that they were going to need substantial quantities of Elastic Rail Spikes, they asked if they could be galvanized.

Other anti-corrosive treatments were certainly given consideration. By July 1945, for example, 4,550 spikes had been despatched to the L.M.S. after having been subjected to the Parkerising process at the railway's request. It seemed that the cost of that method was prohibitive. It came out at 2d per spike. In July 1946 it was reported that the L.M.S. was testing various processes in relation to the spike, chiefly in its laboratory at Derby. The only treated spikes actually installed in track were a Parkerised batch at Weedon and another lot treated with paint at Floriston water-troughs. "Of the four or five different experiments on hand", it seemed, "the most important was galvanizing, which was an unusual treatment for a spring; it looked good but it did not necessarily follow that it was worthwhile. A proper report covering all tests would be made in due course".

And so it was that the L.M.S. was the first of the ERS Company's customers to make a specific request that the spikes should be galvanized. Quotations had been obtained from three firms by the August of 1946. Bayliss, Jones & Bayliss of Wolverhampton had submitted the lowest, and specimens from them showed that the "galvanizing between the leaves of the spike" was better than had been expected. Some spikes had been distorted by heat, but not enough of them to make a fuss about.

The following May the board of the company was told that spikes were still being sent to B.J.B. at Wolverhampton and also that the L.M.S. Research Department was apparently very pleased with the results of its tests of galvanized spikes. Clearly the process did the spikes no harm. It was agreed "that, in view of the possibility of the L.M.S. requiring all future orders to be galvanized, we should ask Elasteel to give consideration to the idea of themselves undertaking this work". At an Elasteel meeting held in Sheffield shortly afterwards Rawes pursued the question of installing a galvanizing plant, and it was arranged that sample spikes should be galvanized in a special chamber at the works of Pyrene Ltd.

But on July 15th 1947 Captain Cowen, Managing Director of Elasteel, wrote in to London to say: "We have approached all the makers of galvanizing plants in the country that we can trace and so far have only found one in any way interested in the job and they, very candidly, warn us against entering the trade. The firm in question is Thompson Bros. (Bilston) Ltd. and we cannot trace that any member of their board has any official connection with any firm of galvanizers who may have the chance of carrying out the process for us". Offers had been made, it seemed, by three firms. One of them had been Wedge & Company, at ten tons a week.

The picture Thompson Bros. painted was black indeed. They said, Cowen's letter went on, "that even if we decide to go ahead it will take at least two years before the plant could be ready and, as spun galvanizing is a specialised job, they could only prepare the plant after consultation with the man who is going to run it and that that man would have to be one who has been trained for the job. Until they, the plant makers, have discussed the job in all its facets with the man who is going to run it, they cannot give us an indication of either its capital cost or the running charges, so we are no further forward than we were and it seems as though, for the time being anyway, we shall have to be content to sub-let the galvanizing."

By October 1947 it had been decided that "as far as possible this work should be done by Cooper in Sheffield". In other words, George Cooper & Sons. Soon however B. E. Wedge Ltd. of Willenhall, Staffordshire, was also helping out, to the tune of up to 100 tons a week. But it was a good eighty miles from Worksop to the Black Country, which meant some hundred and sixty for each round trip. Transport costs were heavy. In March 1949 Rawes raised this matter at an Elasteel meeting, and pressed on with his idea of starting up a plant at Worksop. It was decided to carry out tests so that the susceptibility to rust of spikes treated in various ways could be compared. The results were to determine whether the plant would go in for Parkerising, bonderising or galvanizing.

That August Captain Cowen told Peter Wedge, whose company was by this time doing all the galvanizing, that Elasteel would "shortly be forced to get the spikes galvanized in or near Worksop to reduce the total cost of the process—by eliminating the high cost of carriage to and from Willenhall".

At once Wedge went to see Cowen. He asked whether Elasteel would be interested in starting up a galvanizing plant. On being told that the company at Claylands Forge was already thinking of doing so, Wedge offered to set it up.

Whereupon negotiations quickly began. The plant would be located in the Forge building, and a company would be formed with B. E. Wedge Ltd., Elasteel Ltd. and the ERS Company Ltd. each holding one third of the issued capital. Permission would need to be obtained from the Ministry of Supply, still landlords of the Worksop site, before any part of the premises could be sub-let. The business of the new company would be the galvanizing of spikes, but it was intended that eventually it would also go in for general galvanizing work. Peter Wedge was to be Managing Director, and on the board there was to be one director each from Elasteel Ltd. and the ERS Company.

The Worksop Galvanizing Company Ltd. was incorporated on March 23rd 1950. Half of the shares were in fact held by B. E. Wedge Ltd., and one quarter each by Elasteel and the ERS Company. At the first board meeting, held on April 3rd, W. H. Newson was elected Chairman and Cyril Rodgers appointed Company Secretary. A. B. Gott was the Elasteel representative, alongside Max Pepper, financial director of B. E. Wedge Ltd. Often meetings were to take place at the Royal Victoria Station Hotel in Sheffield, where Rawes always booked his favourite suite.

The previous year had seen the spike taken up as a standard fastening by the new British Railways, and galvanizing had become a firm requirement. However the ERS Company did not agree with a statement published during 1953 which suggested that "all elastic rail spikes should be spun galvanized to prevent corrosion". A correction to this was duly added in the volume where it appeared. "On the home railways," it read, "a large proportion of the lines are situated near the coasts and because of this and the prevailing bad atmospheric conditions, especially in the industrial areas, British Railways use spun galvanized elastic rail spikes to prevent corrosion. It is, however, altogether an exception for elastic rail spikes to be galvanized for use overseas." And such was the case.

The installation of the plant was almost complete by the end of 1950, but the Ministry of Supply made things difficult by both refusing an allocation of spelter (zinc for galvanizing) and prohibiting the galvanizing of spikes. Even in the May of 1951, the company was still being deprived of "the main source of business it had anticipated", although intensive negotiations had resulted in an allocation of twenty tons of spelter per month being allowed as from March. The company had officially started trading on April 23rd, and orders for general galvanizing work had come in from various firms in the Midlands. There was enough work to keep a day shift going for six months.

Permission to galvanize spikes was at last received, although no-one could be sure how long this would last, and the requirement from Elasteel was for some fifty tons a week. It was, therefore, necessary to maintain a steady output of outside work at the thirty tons a week level as a safeguard. But obtaining enough zinc remained a problem.

The plant was being managed by one of Wedge's men, Peter Cowper-Coles, who was to be succeeded late in 1952 by John Taylor. Another of the original trio of pioneers who started up Worksop Galvanizing was Ben Hind, who is today the only employee of the company to have been with it throughout its existence.

In September 1951 it was reported that "we have received a visit from Mr. Loach and Mr. Hair of the Technical Research Department, British Railways. They appeared to be very satisfied with the way in which we were tackling the galvanizing of the spikes, and took samples with them, which proved to be most satisfactory". By March 1952 spikes were being galvanized at the rate of sixty-five tons a week, and there was forty-five tons a week of outside work. And soon zinc was freely available. It was to come on the free market on January

1st 1953, and when this happened the cost fell rapidly so that a reduction in prices could be made by the company.

The tonnage galvanized steadily increased, and in the year that ended on April 30th 1958 it was up by a thousand tons compared with the year before. 1957–58 had been a peak period for spike production, and the galvanizing works had been expanded to keep up with the flow of business. Yet suddenly at about this point the number of spikes needing treatment began to fall. Efforts to build up outside work were made, but the competition was considerable. At the end of 1958 a weekly collection and delivery service for the Grimsby area was started. Till now the incentive to encourage general galvanizing work had not been all that strong, since spikes provided such a sizeable captive market, even though galvanized spikes were seldom exported. The spike still provided 90% of the company's business.

Captain Cowen, who had been on the board all through these early years, resigned in August 1959, his place being taken by Sanson. The connection between George Turton, Platts and Elasteel having been terminated, the post of Company Secretary to Worksop Galvanizing became vacant, since Cyril Rodgers was a G.T.P. man. Len Gardner took over in January 1960. And in October that year B. E. Wedge Ltd.'s interest in the company was bought out. Rawes became Chairman, since Newson wanted to cut down on his activities, while Peter Wedge remained on the board in a consultative capacity.

A fruitful dialogue developed between Wedge, who as the galvanizing expert used traditional methods for costing work on the spike, and Len Gardner who as Company Secretary was requested to investigate costing methods. Costing was the secret of the galvanizing business. The current costing practice was inaccurate. The goods you treated were weighed, since this was the only way you could measure them. No real distinction was made between one ton of goods and another in relation to surface area. So the customer with heavy goods benefited, since the price system favoured him.

As a result of Len Gardner's investigations, a revised pricing basis was established. It was essential to get the costing right, for it was in heavy goods that the profit lay. This realistic new approach to it, coupled with the new style of management Gardner and Parratt championed, was to play a large part in helping the galvanizing business out of the cottage industry era. Ron Parratt was appointed Assistant Company Secretary of W.G.C. in January 1961, and he built up the commercial side of the business.

The drive for outside work went on, particularly on the northeast coast. "The time might come," commented Newson in February 1961, "when galvanizing spikes became a minor item and outside work a major item in the company's sales". Sanson now took the helm as Managing Director, and when Rawes resigned that August he became Chairman as well. John Taylor was followed as General Manager by Ron Parratt.

The introduction of the Pandrol Clip meant that the demand for galvanized spikes was bound to shrink drastically. Nor was Pandrol itself in the galvanizing market, since it did not require this process—and was later simply painted with black bitumastic. The continuous flexing of the new fastening made galvanizing unnecessary. And you did not galvanize if you could avoid it, for the treatment tended to eat into the skin of the steel to get a good binding and stresses were then accentuated. Pandrol Clips, in any case, being made from heavy section round bar, were less subject to the incidence of corrosion than other rail fastenings.

British Railways' standardisation on Pandrol and Lockspikes for use with timber sleepers did, however, mean that the demand for galvanized Lockspikes was boosted. Yet the writing was on the wall. The future of the company, if there was to be one, would have to lie in the general galvanizing field.

So Parratt boldly led the company into the arena. Before long 90% of its galvanizing output consisted of outside work. The old proportion had been reversed. And W.G.C. found that it had become one of the top ten general galvanizers in the country. At first the plant had not been suitable for general work on such a scale, and new plant had had to be added. New markets, too, had needed seeking out.

Worksop was not an ideal location for a galvanizing company. There was no business there. The area which did prove fruitful was Tees-side, and as a result the under-lease of a former War Department depot was taken in November 1968 from Redcar Welding Company. It was at Marske-by-the-Sea, on the outskirts of Redcar. And in April 1969 the business of Redcar Galvanizers was bought. Now the company had a foot on the ground in the right place. It could establish a genuine local 'presence' in Tees-side, and provide an on-the-spot service for urgent small scale needs. Soon a small plant was in action, with twenty-five people running it.

On January 1st 1967 Parratt was appointed Works Director and Jack Marshall was to be the new General Manager under him. Sanson resigned as Chairman and Managing Director at the end of December 1969, and George Flint occupied the chair for a brief spell before he too resigned and Trevor Astley took over. On January 14th 1971 Peter Wedge resigned from the board, to concentrate his energies upon being a friendly competitor.

During 1971 a throughput of 400 tons in one week was achieved, and a total of 19,344 tons was galvanized, representing a sales turnover of £546,000. In the November it was agreed "that to ensure the continuation of the company's business and to safeguard its profits, it was now necessary to consider the first stage for the renewal of plant and the extension of capacity at Worksop, bearing in mind that the lease at Redcar lapsed in 1981". The building of a new plant on a

site next door to Claylands Forge, at an estimated cost of
£150,000, was eventually begun by way of a move towards
taking W.G.C. out of the rail fastening domain. It was sche-
duled for opening in October 1973.

Galvanizing goes on at the existing plant twenty-four
hours a day. Outside work undertaken includes everything
from wheelbarrows and manhole covers to motorway crash
barriers, lamp posts to nails, nuts and bolts, power pylons and
agricultural barns to fabricated girders. On the rail fastening
side, the reconditioning of old screwspikes has been carried
out for British Railways.

W.G.C. operates a daily collection and delivery service—
sixty miles eastwards to Grimsby and the coast, eighty miles
south as far as Burton-on-Trent, and 130 miles north to the
Hartlepools. Worksop has a fleet of nine lorries, while Redcar
has two more to cope with the Newcastle area. A good deal
of work is done on an onward transmission basis. That is to
say, it is collected from the customer, brought to Worksop and
galvanized, and then taken direct to the site where it is required. Once it leaves his factory, the customer does not see
it there again.

So much for the Worksop Galvanizing Company, an
instructive example of the art of diversification. But there was
to be another, this time in close connection with the mining
field. The selling rights in Britain for a type of mining roof
bolt developed in South Africa were acquired during 1968,
and by the following year the product was being manufactured
at Claylands Forge. The inventor was a mining engineer named
Louis Gabriel Jacobus Corbett, who when devising his system
of strata bolting had been given much assistance by another
engineer with the name of Arthur Askey. Corbett and his thrust-
ing young son Bob had formed a company known as Torque
Tension Bolt Co. (Pty.) Ltd. in order to manufacture and market
the device. It was based at Heidelberg in the Transvaal.

J

A British company was incorporated on February 21st 1968 under the name of Torque Tension (UK) Limited, as a member of the ERS Group. An agreement with the South African company took effect on July 31st. Half the shares were held by the ERS Company, and half by the South Africans, the two Corbetts taking seats on the board.

On October 15th 1969 another company was incorporated— in Queensland, Australia. This was Torque Tension (Australia) Pty. Ltd., which was owned equally by Torque Tension (UK) Ltd. and Evans Deakin Industries Ltd. of Brisbane. It had already been decided, in the July of 1968, that the exclusive territory of the British company was to be "all countries of the world excluding: Australia and New Zealand, Canada, Bolivia, Peru, Chile, Botswana, Madagascar, Malawi, Mozambique, the Republic of South Africa, Rhodesia, Swaziland, Zambia, Lesotho".

The Chairman, O. B. Bennett, C.B.E., resigned on August 31st 1970, after having done a great deal to encourage both the company's inception and its growth. His successor was Trevor Astley. December 16th of the same year saw the company being voluntarily wound up and replaced by another known simply as Torque Tension Limited (which in fact had been incorporated six days earlier). Astley was again Chairman, and the shareholdings remained on the same fifty-fifty basis. With the acquisition of the South African shares the following June, Torque Tension Ltd. became a wholly owned subsidiary of the Group.

By this time all the roof bolts available for sale were being produced at Worksop, although the components were still being imported from South Africa. In February 1972 it was agreed that "in future all components would be purchased from U.K. suppliers". The General Manager at Worksop, M. R. Stokes, joined the board in August 1972 in place of M. R. Corbett, to whose foresight and enthusiasm the directors paid tribute. L. G. J. Corbett had resigned in the June of the previous year.

The essence of the Torque Tension system of strata bolting was the use of the mechanical expansion bolt. You had an expanding malleable iron shell into which you screwed. You got your initial anchorage with the torque (the rotating movement), and then came the tension. This loaded the bolt so that the ground was pre-stressed to give reliable local support. The method could be applied swiftly and simply, and it offered safe anchorage even in strata that were friable (likely to crumble).

But there was also another way, involving a resin-bonded roof bolt. In this case you had a resin sack which broke and set in a lump as you drove your bolt in. This method was particularly suitable where you had weaker strata broken ground. The resin was manufactured by I.C.I. Ltd.

Considerable resistance to the system was met in this country at first, and had to be overcome. Perhaps it was felt that miners themselves might object to such an insubstantial looking method of securing roofs, despite the fact that it offered greater safety than traditional methods. Ultimately substantial expansion of the company depended upon the tactics of the National Coal Board, which had not yet fixed on a policy of systematic bolting as a means of roof support.

An export trade was beginning slowly, and a regular market had been established in Ghana's Ashanti Goldfields. There had been some deliveries to Ireland and to Zambia. Total sales in 1971 amounted to 225,000 bolts and 788,000 resin capsules, representing a sales turnover of £438,000.

Other products marketed by the company soon included hydraulic drilling machines for mines. These were designed by Manor Technical Services Ltd., a company 49% of whose equity was bought by the ERS Company on September 1st 1972.

Torque Tension Ltd. was appointed exclusive agent for the

J*

sale of the Pandrol Assembly to the National Coal Board in
1972, and the company's sales personnel were to be instructed
in the advantages of not only Pandrol but also Lockspikes and
Elastic Rail Spikes, so that they could promote them during
their visits to mines.

The Present Set-up—and the Future

The Elastic Rail Spike Company had been conceived in the somewhat infertile environment of creosote and weedkiller. It had been born into the realms of railway engineering, and had come of age in 1958 flourishing a new technological triumph in the shape of the 'Pandrol' Rail Clip. And in 1960 it was to marry—into a mining family of high repute. How did the courtship begin?

The principal shareholders in the company were Bernuth, Lembcke Co., Inc. and L. N. Rawes. By the end of the 1950s the American interest, never actively participatory, was just about dormant. Rawes was advancing in years, and he wanted to sell. In order to realise his capital gain, he could easily have approached an organisation already involved in the rail fastening field. Had he done so, such a buyer would doubtless have taken over all the patents, and Stewart Sanson to boot, but effectively dispensed with the rest of the company. Yet Rawes wanted his offspring to stay intact. So he looked elsewhere, seeking a purchaser who had no railway expertise.

It so happened that one of the people with whom Rawes shared an enthusiasm for golf was the Chairman of a mining finance house called Central Mining & Investment Corporation Ltd. He was Sir Archibald Forbes, C.B.E. The relationship which was soon to spring up between Central Mining and the Elastic Rail Spike Company stemmed from this initial common interest.

During 1960 the ERS Company became a wholly owned subsidiary of Central Mining, which by 1965 was itself to form a constituent part of a new and much larger finance group—Charter Consolidated Limited.

On December 30th 1960 the two-hundred-and-first board meeting of the Elastic Rail Spike Company was attended by three representatives of Centramic U.K. Ltd., Central Mining's holding company. They were Derek Pollen, George Flint and J. D. Ballardie. The whole of the issued share capital of the ERS Company, with the exception of just a few shares, was transferred to Centramic U.K. Ltd., and Pollen and Flint were appointed directors. Ned Rawes retired on the following August 31st, and was succeeded as Chairman by S. D. H. Pollen who paid tribute to "the vitality and enthusiasm of the ERS Company Ltd. staff which was obviously due to the leadership of Mr. L. N. Rawes". Flint became Deputy Chairman. Bill Newson was to remain on the board until his retirement on March 31st 1964.

O. M. Bernuth had last attended a board meeting on November 18th 1947, together with his son C. M. Bernuth. Charles Bernuth, unlike his brother Patrick, had not been a director of the company. But he was quite a character. When in London he used to stay at the Ritz, where he kept a bicycle. He rode everywhere on it, believing this was the only way to get to know the place. Both Oscar Bernuth and Patrick had resigned as directors of the ERS Company on January 1st 1958. Very shortly afterwards the board had noted "with the utmost regret the death on 14th January 1958 of Mr. O. M. Bernuth who was one of the original directors of the company and directed the Secretary to convey to Mr. E. P. Bernuth their deep sympathy in the loss which he and this company has sustained".

Bernuth, Lembcke Co., Inc. vacated its offices in Mincing Lane on September 29th 1961. The old connection had at last come, rather sadly, to an end. During the war there had been a degree of interchangeability amongst the small staff, first in Fenchurch Street and then in Mincing Lane, which ran the offices of Bernuth, Lembcke Co., Inc., Bernuth's Adellen Shipping Company and the ERS Company. Bernuth, Lembcke, who had owned tankers before the war, had then found themselves managing 17,000-ton T.2 tankers and Liberty ships for the U. S. Government. The Adellen Shipping Company's tanker *Adellen*, named after Ada and Ellen, the wives of Bernuth's two sons, had been several times damaged by bombs before being torpedoed in the Atlantic. After the war another vessel of the same name had carried this one-ship company's flag.

In wartime, the Bernuth, Lembcke tankers had loaded up with creosote oil at the Port of London, Cardiff, Grangemouth, Immingham and Newcastle. Often the loading and discharging had gone on when the port had been under a hail of bombs, as Thomas Johnston (the ERS Company's Secretary) had cause to remember well. Another man who, after the war, had worked with the tankers was Len Gardner, who had joined the ERS Company via Bernuth, Lembcke.

Johnston retired as Company Secretary on April 10th 1964, after having served for thirty-four years with first Bernuth, Lembcke and then the ERS Company. L. T. Gardner succeeded him.

Derek Pollen was to relinquish the chair at the end of December 1964, following his appointment as a director of Charter Consolidated Ltd., and George Flint was to take over as Chairman. It was at this time that Charter came into being, and the Elastic Rail Spike Company found itself belonging to one of the largest and most important mining and investment organisations in the world. Central Mining had, in fact, now merged with Consolidated Mines Selection Ltd., a British mining and investment company, and with the British South Africa Company, one of the original Charter companies. The new Group was registered on December 18th 1964, and by 1965 it had been securely welded into a single entity.

As a result of the merger, the ERS Company moved from its offices at 41/43 Mincing Lane and into 7 Rolls Buildings, Fetter Lane, where by the beginning of 1966 it was firmly ensconced. Sanson insisted on having the best office, with an adjacent bathroom to go with it. And of course he got both. Yet he was not to enjoy such sybaritic luxury for all that long. On December 31st 1969 he retired, and brought to an end a period of service extending over thirty-two years. It had been his skill, drive and vision which had provided the company with the key to success. Indeed, it was difficult to imagine things going on without him.

They did, of course. Trevor Astley became Managing Director on January 1st 1970. And when George Flint retired as Chairman at the end of March, his place was taken by R. H. Dent, the Chairman of Cape Asbestos, a substantial company in which Charter had a controlling interest. Dent himself resigned at the end of 1972 and on January 1st 1973 J. G. Richardson took the chair.

The Elastic Rail Spike Company Ltd. Group today consists of the Elastic Rail Spike Company Ltd. (ERS) London, which is the holding company, and of its subsidiaries Pandrol Ltd., Lockspike Ltd., Elasteel Ltd., Worksop Galvanizing Company Ltd. and Torque Tension Ltd. There are also the associate companies—Manor Technical Services in the U.K. and others abroad—together with the licensed manufacturers overseas in whose companies the ERS Company has no financial interest. There are licensees in Austria, Belgium, Brazil, Finland, India and Mexico.

What now lies ahead? A new era of expansion is at hand. The first delivery of Pandrol Clips to Spain has been arranged through the newly formed company, Pandrol Iberica Ltda., and negotiations for the setting up of Pandrol Canada Ltd.

are well under way. Successful trial installations in West Germany reveal the need for starting up a manufacturing company in Western Europe.

In October 1973 a dinner dance was held in Sheffield for the employees of the company and their wives and for a number of overseas friends. It marked a milestone in the company's history—the production of the 360-millionth rail fastening at Worksop.

The Claylands Forge plant is working to capacity and more machines are to be installed during 1974 to cope with the ever-growing demands of British Rail and of customers overseas.

At the L. S. Sanson Development Centre, the extension and refining of design work continues in relation both to Pandrol fastenings and to developments stemming from them. Many challenging problems are being faced—and solved. Applications for continuous concrete track beds, for example. Not to speak of the demands of trains that will shift at 200 m.p.h. or more, and of 20,000-ton iron ore trains with enormous axle loads.

The new recruits to the Group's ranks have an even more sizeable future ahead of them than their pioneering predecessors had. The world is rapidly moving into the new railway age. They are ready for it.

Postscript

John Milligan has ably set out the history of the Elastic Rail Spike Group, detailing its growth from the early days of the resilient pioneers. What now of the future?

The present generation is just as resilient as the original pioneers and has the advantage of starting from well prepared ground. Design, development and marketing staff, hand picked for their missionary zeal, have increased in numbers and are steadily spreading the Pandrol gospel through America, Africa and the Far East. At the same time we are firmly cementing friendships formed with British Railways and many others in our early development days. It will be noted that the Pandrol symbol appears at the heading of each chapter of this book. This is now much the most important of our products.

During 1973, more than 15 million rail fastenings were produced at Worksop, bringing the total, since the formation of Elasteel Ltd., to more than 300 million. This represents over 25,000 miles of railway track from home based production alone.

Substantial growth is anticipated in Australia, and new associate companies will appear in North America and Europe when demand builds up. At home, industrial and mining railways are beginning to follow British Railways practice, and ever increasing export requirements maintain a steady pressure for expansion on the Worksop plant.

Extensions to the galvanizing plant, coming into operation in 1973, will soon be inadequate for a growing countrywide business and new, more extensive premises for Torque Tension are already planned for erection in 1974.

Probably the most important asset of the Group, in its world-wide sense, is the quality of its people at all levels, from shop floor to boardroom. From the start, only the best has been good enough, and this remains the policy today.

The accounts of Sam Oldfield and his colourful visits to distant lands typify the determination to ensure our high standards are maintained wherever the Group's products are manufactured. Most of us, however, work at a less spectacular level, some standing daily at machines and other coping with the inevitable paper work that any business generates. It is the constant endeavour of people at all levels that in the long term ensures the success and steady growth of the ERS family.

As we go to press, notification has been received that the 'Pandrol' Rail Fastening Assembly as used on concrete sleepers is the subject of a Design Council Award, 1974.

April 1974   *Trevor Astley*

References

Chapter 1

For the origins of railways, see: W. O. Henderson, *The Indus-trialization of Europe: 1780–1914* (Thames & Hudson, 1969), p. 43; Horace Greenleaf and G. Tyers, *The Permanent Way* (*Britain's Railroads in the Making*) (Winchester Publications Ltd., 1948), pp. 85–88; R. A. Buchanan, *Industrial Archaeology in Britain* (Pelican Books, 1972), pp. 305–310; Maurice Ashley, *Life in Stuart England* (B. T. Batsford Ltd., 1964), p. 6; also entries in *Chambers's Encyclopaedia, Vol. VIII* (1866), under "Railways"; *Chambers's Encyclopaedia* (1967), under "Railway"; *Harmsworth's Universal Encyclopedia, Vol 8* (1922), article by A. Williams, under "Railways"; *Encyclopaedia Britannica, Vol. 18* (1970), under "Railways".

The development of the rail and of rail fastenings during the nineteenth century is either described or touched upon in Greenleaf and Tyers, *The Permanent Way*, cited above, pp. 92–100 and 118–119; James Hodge, *Richard Trevithick* (*Lifelines 6*) (Shire Publications Ltd., 1973), p. 22; Donald J. Smith, *Robert Stephenson* (*Lifelines 8*) (Shire Publications Ltd., 1973), pp. 23, 25 and 32; and in *The Track of the Future*, an article by H. Langford Lewis in the Feb. 1942 issue of *Railways*.

The reference to "the patent of Mr. Birkenshaw" is from Olinthus J. Vignoles, *Life of Charles Blacker Vignoles . . . Soldier and Civil Engineer* (Longmans, Green, & Co., 1889), p. 154; other references and quotations from the same source are taken from pp. 182–183, 201, 222–223 and 225. There are useful entries on Vignoles and on Joseph Locke, George and Robert Stephenson, Sir Marc Brunel and I. K. Brunel in

Sidney Lee (editor), *Dictionary of National Biography* (1893). The quotations relating to Locke are from Joseph Devey, *The Life of Joseph Locke* (Richard Bentley, 1862), p. 111. Another useful source is Locke himself, *Address of Joseph Locke, Esq. M.P. on his election as President of the Institution of Civil Engineers, Session 1857–58* (Wm. Clowes & Sons, 1858), pp. 20–21. See also Terry Coleman, *The Railway Navvies* (Hutchinson, 1965; Pelican Books, 1968), Chapter 7.

For general background, consult David Thomson, *England in the Nineteenth Century* (Penguin Books, 1950), pp. 41–42 and 137–139; also David Thomson, *Europe Since Napoleon* (Longmans, 1957; revised edition, Pelican Books, 1966), pp. 178–182 (Pelican edition). The quotation is from the latter, p. 178. The reference to Brunel's rails being used for fencing is from R. A. Buchanan, *Industrial Archaeology in Britain* (already cited), p. 315.

The technical background is well covered in Ronald A. Inglis, *An Introduction to Railway Engineering* (Chapman & Hall, 1953), Chapter IV; R. A. Hamnett (editor), *British Railway Track: Design, Construction and Maintenance* (The Permanent Way Institution, 1943; 3rd edition, 1964), Chapters II and IV; and in Greenleaf and Tyers, *The Permanent Way* (already cited), pp. 5–25. For the reference to spikes being known as 'nails', see letter from H. L. Holland of Hamilton, Ontario in *Railway World*, March 1973, p. 129.

Chapter 2

The statistics on track mileages in the U.S.A. are taken from *Chambers's Encyclopaedia* (1967), which itself used as its source the *Directory of Railway Officials & Year Book* (1960–61). The quotation in the opening paragraph is from Robert Littell, *Slowing Wheels* (article in *Transatlantic*, Nov. 1943, p. 49).

The Vignoles quotation is from O. J. Vignoles, *Life of Charles Blacker Vignoles* (already cited), pp. 183–4, while the

K

quotation following this is from *Chambers's Encyclopaedia, Vol. VIII* (1866), entry on "Railways". For the expectation of life of crossties in the U.S., after creosoting, see *Encyclopaedia Britannica* (1970), under "Railways". For creosoting processes, see George M. Hunt and George A. Garrett, *Wood Preservation* (McGraw-Hill Book Co., 1938; 2nd edition, 1953), pp. 10, 205–206 and 208; Greenleaf and Tyers, *The Permanent Way* (already cited), pp. 45–46; Ronald A. Inglis, *An Introduction to Railway Engineering* (already cited), Chapter IV; R. A. Hamnett (editor), *British Railway Track* (already cited), Chapter II.

On weedkilling, see again Greenleaf and Tyers, *The Permanent Way*, p. 47. For the Vignoles quotation, see O. J. Vignoles, *Life of Charles Blacker Vignoles* (already cited), pp. 182–183.

W. K. Wallace's words are from his paper *Recent Innovations in Track Maintenance and Design*, prepared for a booklet issued in connection with the Diamond Jubilee of the Permanent Way Institution, 1944. They are quoted in the Minutes of the 55th Meeting of Directors of the ERS Co. Ltd., October 5th 1944.

See also *The Railway Gazette* of April 7th 1967 (article on *Elastic Rail Spike Development*).

Chapter 3
Broken Hill: see Leonie I. Paddison, *The Railways of New South Wales: 1855–1955* (The Dept. of Railways, New South Wales), p. 88. For N. W. Swinnerton's paper read before the Permanent Way Institution, see H. Langford Lewis, *The Track of the Future* (article, already cited, in Feb. 1942 issue of *Railways*).

Chapter 4
W. H. Newson's views on the question of enemy-held shares are reported in the Minutes of the 41st Meeting of Directors

of the ERS Co. Ltd., June 21st 1943. The Minutes of the 62nd
Meeting, June 14th 1945, include L. N. Rawes' remarks
apropos the reconstruction of the company, while those for
the Extraordinary General Meeting of August 31st 1945 detail
the financial losses quoted.

R. Bridgman's letter about the problems of getting spikes
driven correctly in Nigeria is mentioned in the Minutes of the
62nd Directors' Meeting of the ERS Co. Ltd., June 14th
1945, and his second letter, dated November 13th 1945,
is quoted in the Minutes of the 6th Meeting of the reconstituted
company, December 4th 1945. Mr. Bilham's letter to Rawes
is quoted in the Minutes of the 44th Directors' Meeting,
Sept. 21st 1943. N. W. Swinnerton's comments are given in
the same Minutes. Swinnerton's message of Nov. 29th 1944
about the prestige of the spike is mentioned in the Minutes of
the 56th Directors' Meeting, Dec. 7th 1944.

On the steel famine, see the entry in *Keesing's Contemporary
Archives* for April 19th–26th, 1947. On the nationalisation of
Britain's railways, see *Encyclopaedia Britannica, Vol. 18* (1970),
under "Railways".

Chapter 5

On the post-war period in general, consult David Thomson,
Europe Since Napoleon (already cited), p. 821. For Perón and
Argentina, see *Encyclopaedia Britannica* (1970), under "Perón"
and under "Argentina"; also entry in *Keesing's Contemporary
Archives* for April 26th–May 3rd 1947; *The Sunday Times
Magazine* for Sept. 26th 1971 (survey by Norman Lewis on
Latin America).

For the carbon content of steel, see William Alexander and
Arthur Street, *Metals in the Service of Man* (Pelican Books,
1944; 5th edition, 1972), pp. 66 and 155–161. On Hay and
Goldstein's visit to Europe, the source is the article *Modern
European Developments in Permanent Way Engineering* by A.

Goldstein and J. G. Hay, in the July 1953 issue of *Die Suid-Afrikaanse Instituut van Siviele Ingenieure*.

Chapter 6

On Wayland Smith, see Brian Branston, *The Lost Gods of England* (Thames & Hudson, 1967), Chapter I; H. S. Robinson and Knox Wilson (Barbara Leonie Picard, editor), *The Encyclopaedia of Myths and Legends of all Nations* (Edmind Ward, 1962), under "Wayland Smith"; Dorothy Whitelock, *The Beginnings of English Society* (Pelican Books, 1952), pp. 116–117. "Clayland Wharfs" are indicated on the *Map of County of Nottingham, from an Actual Survey made 1824–25 by C. & J. Greenwood* (Greenwood & Co., 1831).

Chapter 7

Sense of urgency in British railway engineers: see Terry Coleman, *The Railway Navvies* (already cited), p. 205. On the Elastic Rail Spike versus the Macbeth spike, see Ronald A. Inglis, *An Introduction to Railway Engineering* (already cited), Chapter IV. On welded track in Australia, see Leonie I. Paddison, *The Railways of New South Wales* (already cited), p. 142. The first use of welded rail in the U.S.A. is mentioned in *Encyclopaedia Britannica*, Vol. *18* (1970) under "Railways".

The reference to Robert Stephenson is from Donald J. Smith, *Robert Stephenson* (already cited), p. 25.

Chapter 8

On the background to the Hedjaz Railway, see H. St. John Philby, *The Land of Midian* (Ernest Benn, 1957), pp. 3, 10, 15–16, 57, 96, 113–114, 122, 126, 165 and 168–169; James Morris, *The Hashemite Kings* (Faber & Faber, 1959), pp. 21, 28–30, 50 and 105; Robert C. Kingsbury, *An Atlas of Middle Eastern Affairs* (Methuen, 1964), p. 24; David Howarth, *The Desert King: A Life of Ibn Saud* (Collins, 1964), pp. 78–79 and

224–225; and T. E. Lawrence, *Seven Pillars of Wisdom* (privately printed, 1926; Jonathan Cape, 1935; Penguin edition, 1962), pp. 49, 51, 117, 251, 376, 440–441 and 540. The Lawrence quotation is from Chapter LXVI (p. 376). See also David Thomson, *Europe Since Napoleon* (already cited), pp. 470, 518 and 631.

For the Six-Day War of June 1967, see Edgar O'Ballance, *The Third Arab-Israeli War* (Faber & Faber, 1972); James P. Warburg, *Crosscurrents in the Middle East* (Gollancz, 1969), pp. 200–208; *Keesing's Contemporary Archives* (entry for May 23rd 1967, etc.).

The cancellation of the original contract—awarded to the Saudi Arabian Ladin Company and the Japanese firm Marubini-Ida—is reported in the *Financial Times* of Sept. 27th 1963. The contract for British steel is reported in the *Daily Telegraph* of Jan. 18th 1967. See also the *Guardian* of March 31st 1973 (Susannah Honeyman on *The right side of the tracks*).

Chapter 9

On the galvanizing of spikes, see Ronald A. Inglis, *An Introduction to Railway Engineering* (already cited), Chapter IV, and note the significant correction made on the insert.

Chapter 10

On Charter Consolidated Ltd., see *Kompass*; the *Mining International Yearbook, 1972–3*; also the *Charter Annual Report and Accounts* for the year currently ended.

Much publicity has been given in the press to the H.S.T. (High Speed Train) and the A.P.T. (Advanced Passenger Train). See, for example, the *Guardian* of Sept. 19th 1972 (p. 23) and Sept. 20th 1972 (p. 15), and of Aug. 3rd 1972 (David McIlwain on *Quicker and quicker by rail*). On other developments, see *The Times* of Feb. 12th 1973 (Patrick O' Leary on *Investment by British Rail likely to exceed £3m*).

Note: Apart from one or two exceptions which will have been noted, the multitudinous references to the Minutes of the various companies of the Group, and to the files or correspondence and office notes, have not been listed. These, however, are the sources from which—together with the recollections of company people both past and present—the narrative set out in this history has principally been built.

Index

Abdul Hamid II, Sultan, 94, 95
Abdullah, the Amir, 96
Abercynon, 3
Adams, Sir Maurice, 100
Adellen, 123
Adellen Shipping Company, 123
Albania, 22
Alderton Construction Westminster Ltd., 99
Ali, the Amir, 96
Alice Springs, 88
Allenby, General, 96
Allied Post-War Requirements Bureau, 32
Allis Chalmers, 40
American Railway Engineering Association, 91
Amman, 96, 100, 103, 105, 106, 107
Angola, 57
Aqaba, 96, 102, 103
Arabia, 95
Arab Security, 106, 107
Argentina, 18, 24, 44, 46, 56, 57
Argentine State Railways, 46
Armstrong Siddeley Cheetah engine, 60
A.R.P., 36
Ashanti Goldfields, 119
Askey, Arthur, 117
Astley, H. T., 57, 70, 83, 90, 91, 100, 116, 118, 124
Attlee, C. R., 37
Australia, 21, 22, 24, 39, 40, 41, 42, 43, 46, 48, 66, 74, 76, 82, 85, 88, 93, 102, 118, 126
Australian Consolidated Industries Ltd., 39
Austria, 55, 64, 82, 89, 92, 124
Austrian Federal Railways, 92

Badawin, 96
Bakewell, 33
Ballardie, J. D., 122
Baltic, 8
Baltimore, 91
Banda, President, 86
Bangalore, 89
Bangkok, 23, 44
Barnett, W. G. S., 52, 53
Basutoland, 54, 82
Bayliss, Jones & Bayliss, 37, 110
B.B.C., 101
Beaumont, Huntingdon, 1
Bechuanaland, 82
Becke–Prinz, 75
Becker G.m.b.H., Dipl. Ing, K., 99
Bedfordshire, 15
Bedouin, 96
Beeching, Dr, 68
Beirut, 102, 107
Belgian Congo, 30
Belgian National Railways, 92
Belgium, 82, 92, 124
Bengal-Nagpur Railway, 44
Benguela Railway, 57
Bennett, O. B., 118
Berlin–Baghdad Railway, 95
Bernuth, Ada, 123
Bernuth, C. M., 122
Bernuth, Ellen, 123
Bernuth, E. P., 18, 122
Bernuth, Lembcke Co., Inc., 11, 17, 18, 27, 35, 61, 63, 121, 122, 123
Bernuth, Oscar Max, 8, 10, 11, 12, 13, 14, 17, 18, 27, 29, 122, 123
Best, Doug, 56, 62, 67
Bethell Process, 9
Bilham, Mr, 32